PRACTICAL GUIDES

DATA HANDLING

TEACHING WITHIN THE
NATIONAL CURRICULUM

EDITED BY
DAVID GREEN AND ALAN GRAHAM

Published by Scholastic Publications Ltd,
Villiers House, Clarendon Avenue
Leamington Spa, Warwickshire CV32 5PR

© 1994 Scholastic Publications
Text © The Mathematical Association

Editors Janet Parsons and Noel Pritchard
Assistant Editor Kate Banham
Designer Sue Limb
Illustrator Maureen Bradley
Front cover designed by Liz Harrison;
illustrated by Nancy Anderson
Photographs by John Harris (page 5), Martin
Sookias (pages 13, 31, 53, 75, 87, 117, 127, 153
and 163) and Anne Crabbe (page 61)
Index compiled by Barbara Newby

Grateful thanks to the staff and children of
St Philip and St James CE First School, Oxford,
who are featured in the photographs in this book

Every attempt has been made to trace and
acknowledge the photographers whose pictures
appear in this book. The publisher apologises for any
omissions.

Designed using Aldus Pagemaker
Processed by Typesetters, Birmingham
Artwork by Pages Bureau, Leamington Spa
Printed by Ebenezer Baylis & Son, Worcester

British Library Cataloguing in Publication Data
A catalogue record for this book is available from the
British Library

ISBN 0-590-53145-X

The members of the Mathematical
Association's Teaching Committee sub-
committee, and others who contributed
directly or indirectly to this book at meetings
or by correspondence were:

Andrew Bramwell	Harriet Marland
Andrew Buxton	Tandy Murphy
Sue Cross	Jenny Nixon
Glyn Davies	Arthur Owen
Alan Graham	Pat Perks
David Green	Margaret Rangecroft
Peter Holmes	Mariette Roberts
Jenny Huscroft	Mary Rouncefield
Graham Jepson	Sue Sanders
David Lennox	Hilary Shuard (d. 1993)
Rudolf Lowenstein	Helen Wright

Those mainly responsible for writing this
book were:

Andrew Bramwell	Pat Perks
Andrew Buxton	Margaret Rangecroft
Glyn Davies	Mary Rouncefield
Alan Graham	Hilary Shuard
David Green	Helen Wright
Peter Holmes	

Enquiries can be directed to:
The Mathematical Association, 259 London
Road, Leicester LE2 3BE.

Page 28: *Extract from the 1881 Census*
Crown copyright material in the Public Record Office
is reproduced by permission of the Controller of Her
Majesty's Stationery Office.
Page 39: *Extract from the Intercity timetable*
Reproduced with the permission of Intercity Midland,
a business sector of the British Railways Board.
© 1993 British Railways Board.
Page 48: *Extract from David Moore's 'Uncertainty'*
Reproduced with permission from *On the Shoulders of
Giants – New Approaches to Numeracy.* © 1990 The
National Academy of Sciences. Courtesy of the
National Academy Press, Washington, D.C.
Page 49: *The Crisp Survey*
Reproduced with permission from *Junior Pinpoint –
A Child's Guide to Data Handling* © Longman
Logotron, 1994.
Page 51: *Probability workcards*
Reproduced with permission from the DIME
Probabililty Pack © Geoff Giles, published by DIME
Projects, G15 Speedwell Way, Harleston Industrial
Estate, NORFOLK IP20 9EH.

Contents

Foreword

18th March 1992

To the Mathematical Association

Dear Sir,

I am a primary teacher and am writing to encourage you to put together a book for teachers on data handling. I think this book is greatly needed for two main reasons. Firstly, the subject is relatively new and has been given great prominence in the National Curriculum. Secondly, like many other teachers, I lack background knowledge and confidence myself in this area.

Children are certainly interested in statistics - you only have to look at sales of books like the <u>Guinness Book of Records</u>, and children's interest in music charts and football league tables. I've seen reception children watch me fill in the circles and dashes of the register, fascinated by the pattern and fully understanding that the symbols mean something.

In the past I always thought of statistics as a high powered subject suitable only for upper secondary and tertiary students, and I need help in making it relevant and interesting for the much younger children in my class. I feel strongly that data handling can provide a context and purpose for a lot of the otherwise boring number work that children are already doing at Key Stages 1 and 2, but I need help in understanding the key ideas and am looking for suggestions for classroom activities that will bring them alive for my children. I hope that you can put together a publication that will meet the needs of teachers like myself.

Yours sincerely,

Andrew Bramwell

26th March 1994

Dear Andrew,

Sorry that this book took rather longer to write than we thought. We gathered together a team of primary teachers like yourself, middle school teachers, statistical educators and statisticians, and this book is the result. We hope you find it helpful!

Yours sincerely,

Alan T. Graham and David Green

Introduction
Data handling in the primary school curriculum

'I really thought that all children had the same ability to cross the road – but they don't, do they?'
'This has made me realise I must be much more careful in Cambridge and Royston.'
'Children from busy city schools were not the best at judging the speeds, distances and times of oncoming traffic... they are over confident.'

These three quotations are all from a group of pupils who had been doing a project on how long it took children to decide if it was safe to cross a road, and how long it took them actually to cross it. They timed pupils from different backgrounds (for example, rural, city, small town) in different situations, and these quotations are some of the conclusions they made. They were handling data. They were doing statistics.

5

Data handling and statistics: what are they?

The emphasis on data handling in the National Curriculum has made many teachers ask 'What is data handling?', 'How does it relate to statistics?' and 'Why are we being asked to teach it?' The example on page 5 illustrates some of the answers to these questions.

In many ways 'data handling' is just a new way of saying 'statistics'. If you look at the content of the Handling Data strand in the National Curriculum you will find a very large overlap with secondary school syllabuses in statistics. To some people statistics has overtones of something difficult, theoretical and remote. Although this is a false impression, it is helpful to use a different phrase – data handling – which conveys the importance of collecting and using real data. As well as 'data handling', the word 'statistics' can mean the raw data (usually numbers), or representative numbers derived from the raw data (such as the average).

On its own, the Handling Data strand in the National Curriculum can look very dry and technique-oriented but, when put in the context of the Using and Applying Mathematics strand and taught in the way described in the non-statutory guidance, it comes alive.

Data handling (or statistics in its broader meaning) can be summarised as follows:

'A practical subject devoted to the obtaining and processing of data with a view to making statements, called inferences, which often extend beyond the data. The subject is concerned with the production of good data; this comes from considering experimental designs and sample surveys. It has its origin in real data and is concerned with the processing of data in the widest of contexts and with a wide variety of applications.' (Statement adapted from a definition of statistics given in *Teaching Statistics 11 – 16*, Schools Council Project on Statistical Education.)

In this book we shall use the term 'data handling' with its emphasis on activity; the term 'statistics' will arise in its more restricted meaning of data or data-derived numbers.

The components of data handling

The primary school pupils quoted earlier who were investigating crossing the road safely were involved in data handling (or 'doing statistics') because they were asking clear questions, obtaining good and appropriate data, analysing the data with a view to answering the questions, and drawing useful inferences from the data. Data handling is a practical subject and the motivation behind it is to enable people to solve problems, particularly where there is uncertainty or variability in the outcomes. It is a subject that arises naturally as soon as you start to count and measure sets of things, and when you are trying to find out people's opinions.

Data handling gives us a way of approaching problems. Alan Graham, in his book *Investigating Statistics* (Hodder & Stoughton, 1990), uses the acronym **PCAI** to spell out the four main stages of this type of approach.

Stage P – Posing the question

The **P** stands for **Pose**. Pose the question – in such a way that it is clear what needs to be observed and then measured or counted to work towards an answer. The first questions children pose tend to be general, and need to be made more specific so that it is clear what data are needed. The primary school pupils in our example started with the question 'Is the Green Cross Code good enough?' They made it more specific, and eventually decided on the question 'Are children from city areas better able to estimate whether it is safe to cross a road than children from busy rural schools or from quiet rural schools?'

This aspect of data handling is mentioned specifically in the main National Curriculum document in mathematics at Level 4 in the programme of study for Attainment Target 5 as 'specifically an issue for which data are needed'. It is also implicit in all the cross-curricular work described in the non-statutory guidance. Without some purpose, it is easy to fall into the trap of collecting data for its own sake. This can give a very false impression of the subject, making it seem irrelevant.

Stage C – Collecting the data

The **C** is for **Collect**. Collect the data. If the question has been well posed then it becomes clearer what needs to be measured or counted. The pupils measured how long it took children to decide whether it would be safe to cross, how long it took the vehicle to travel from the corner when it first came into sight to where they were standing, and (later, when the road was safe) how long it took pupils to cross the road. To collect the data

they had to design a data collection sheet as in the Level 2 programme of study. Generally, this aspect of the process is well covered in the programmes of study and statements of attainment at all levels. For younger pupils the emphasis is more on surveys than on experimental data, but both are important.

Stage A – Analysing the data

The **A** is for **Analyse**. Analyse the data. This will involve calculations, graphical and pictorial representation, and other ways of getting relevant information from the data. Amongst other things, the pupils in our examples counted how many city pupils did not give themselves time to cross the road safely and how many rural pupils would not have crossed when there was plenty of time to do so. The analysis was done using frequency tables, bar charts, pie charts and simple calculations as described in the Levels 2 and 3 programmes of study. Analysis of data plays a major part at all levels of the National Curriculum.

Stage I – Interpreting the results

The **I** is for **Interpret**. Interpret the results. What insight do they give into the original question? The pupils were quite surprised to find that the children from a busy rural school were best. Those from a city school were over-confident; those from a quiet rural school were over-cautious. This sort of inference is covered in the National Curriculum documents by phrases such as 'commenting on the results' (Level 2); 'using a database to find answers to simple questions' (Level 3); and 'interpreting bar-line and line graphs' (Level 4).

The pupils may then go on to pose new questions raised by the interpretation, for example:
- Do pupils who know the Green Cross Code put it into practice?
- How well do pupils know the Green Cross Code?
- Is there a *correlation* between knowledge of the code and ability to cross the road?
- Is there a case for a crossing warden?

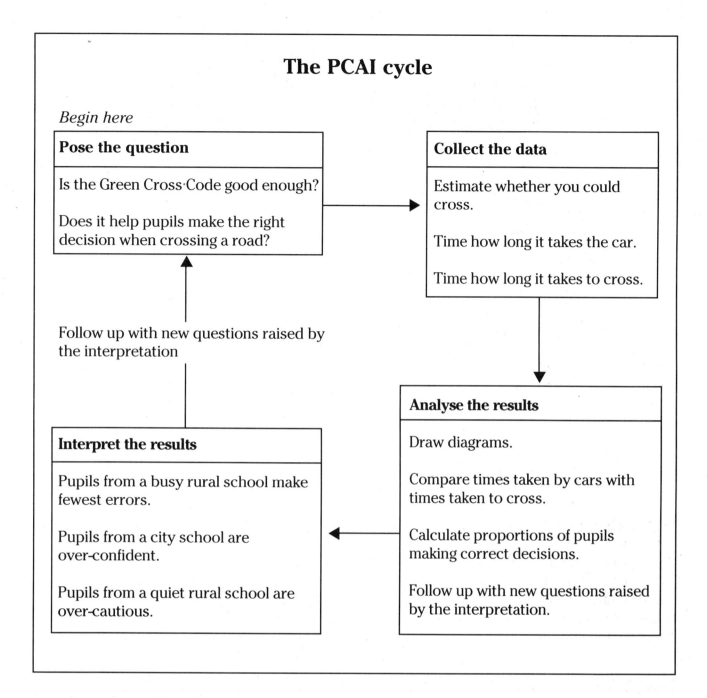

The PCAI cycle

Begin here

Pose the question

Is the Green Cross·Code good enough?

Does it help pupils make the right decision when crossing a road?

Collect the data

Estimate whether you could cross.

Time how long it takes the car.

Time how long it takes to cross.

Follow up with new questions raised by the interpretation

Interpret the results

Pupils from a busy rural school make fewest errors.

Pupils from a city school are over-confident.

Pupils from a quiet rural school are over-cautious.

Analyse the results

Draw diagrams.

Compare times taken by cars with times taken to cross.

Calculate proportions of pupils making correct decisions.

Follow up with new questions raised by the interpretation.

- Does traffic drive faster/slower in cities?
- Are drivers more/less considerate in rural areas?
- Are city school pupils over-confident about other matters?

Why teach data handling?

The fundamental reason for including data handling as part of the general curriculum is that it is part of the culture in which we live. The abilities to think statistically, to deal with statistics and not to be misled by people who draw wrong conclusions from statistical data are important skills needed by all. The process of building up these abilities can, and should, start at a very early age.

Data handling is an important part of the decision making that we all have to do. Even the individual's decision on whether it is safe to cross the road is based on estimates of the speed of cars, the probability of making a mistake and the consequences of such a mistake. Statistical work crops up naturally in all parts of the school curriculum wherever inferences have to be drawn from observations that have been measured or counted.

A Tuck Shop problem investigated by Year 2 children

'During break time children were allowed to buy crisps, biscuits, drinks and so on from a tuck shop. Problems arose when favourite drinks sold out quickly and some children missed out. How often did this arise? A daily count was made.

Bubble gum	~~||||~~
Cola	~~||||~~ ~~||||~~
Orange	|||
Lime		
Blackcurrant	|||

Children made a list of their favourite flavours and compared it to the tally chart. Some children drank lime but preferred cola, and so on. After keeping a tally for a period of two weeks, patterns began to emerge and there was enough information to ask the secretary to order more boxes of certain flavours and less of others. This gave opportunities to experience frequency tables, question posing and the practical application of data handling activities.

– How many of each flavour need to be ordered?
– What happens if tastes change?
– What happens to those children who like to vary their choices?

Children were interested in the investigation because it was important to them. They could see the relevance. It also had a direct impact on their lives and provided the chance of seeing that data are collected and used for a purpose.'

To underline some of these important points, above is a report by the teacher of a group of Year 2 children in a West Midlands school who were undertaking a piece of data handling work.

Through collecting and analysing real data, pupils meet with the idea of uncertainty, and the possibility of there being several different possible conclusions. It is not reasonable, or even appropriate, to expect all the data to be collected directly by the pupils. When the data are collected by those who are to analyse them then the term *primary data* is used. Data which have already been collected by other people are called secondary data; these can be just as valid as primary data for answering a problem. Secondary data can be found in atlases, encyclopaedias, publications of the Central Statistical Office, and many other library sources. The children doing the Green Cross Code investigation could have used secondary data on the number of road traffic accidents and the ages of the people involved to supplement their work. Such data are available from the local authority.

Secondary data raise difficulties: questions such as 'Who collected them?', 'How?', 'When?' and 'Why?' should be addressed in order to check that the data are valid, appropriate and trustworthy. These are important aspects of learning how to handle data. In discussion and argument, pupils learn to think and base their conclusions on evidence. They find that the data are often messy and that there is not always a single, clear answer to a question.

The implications for teaching

The approach emphasised in the National Curriculum documents is of data handling as a set of techniques to be taught. This approach obscures the real value of enabling pupils to think statistically. Some of the techniques are easier to use than others – and it is usually right to use the easy techniques before moving on to the harder ones. These techniques need to be taught and used in the context of investigating a problem. The nature and purpose of the investigation determine what techniques and analysis are appropriate.

This means that, as teachers, we need to find *real* problems which *genuinely* require the use of the simplest techniques, so that they can be developed in the context of finding out something. It is even better if these problems, questions or areas of investigation can be based on the pupils' own curiosity, as this motivates them to learn. The examples used in this book will include many areas of the school curriculum and many of children's real interests; very few will originate in a purely mathematical context.

All this may seem difficult but in fact is easier than it appears. Many areas of investigation can be tackled at different levels; there are simple as well as difficult questions that can be asked and answered. Some questions can be both, depending on the interpretation, for example 'Which canned drinks are most popular at school?' This could be investigated very quickly and simply by a show of hands and a tally chart. On the other hand, it could involve a thorough discussion of what the question really means and what questions to ask, and could lead to a carefully controlled term-long, school-wide project involving the monitoring of canned drink consumption and pupil opinion. It might

even include periodically delving into the school bins! You can start with the questions that require the simpler techniques, and gradually move on to those which need the more difficult ones.

Because of the importance of making the work relate to the pupils' real lives, using real data, and tackling real problems, the data handling sections in published primary mathematics schemes are of limited value. Too often these are written in trivial and unexciting contexts. Most of them are geared towards teaching the techniques one at a time, and do not involve pupils in the whole **PCAI** process.

Primary school pupils can learn to look critically at what they have done if it is a problem real to them. The primary school pupils doing the road safety survey wrote: 'All of the testing should have been carried out on the same stretch of road that was unknown to all the children. This would have made the test more fair.'

A lot of motivation for learning comes from the satisfaction of a well-completed project. One of the pupils who worked on the road traffic survey was seen showing the final report to her parents and overheard saying 'It's good isn't it? We did that!'

Throughout this book there are examples of practical situations where the **PCAI** cycle is relevant and helpful. Examples of situations in which questions may be *posed* are given in Chapter 1 and the sorts of data that may be *collected* are discussed in Chapter 2. The *analysis* is highlighted in the chapters on graphs (Chapters 3 and 4), spreadsheets (Chapter 5) and databases (Chapter 6). The final part of the **PCAI** cycle – *interpreting results and drawing conclusions* – is the subject of Chapter 7. There follows a separate chapter devoted to the topic area of probability which can cause difficulties for teachers but which is a rich area for work on data handling (Chapter 8). Chapter 9 is devoted to cross-curricular issues, and a final chapter provides detailed information about resources. The chapters are all largely independent, but the **PCAI** theme is predominant in Chapters 1 to 7, so it would be wise to read these in sequence when you first come to this book.

Chapter One
Data handling through posing questions

Very many schools incorporate topic work into their teaching at Key Stages 1 and 2. While a class project will incorporate activities from a broad range of curriculum areas, this chapter concentrates solely on the possibilities for data handling. We have provided three substantial case studies (one a collaborative project shared between two classes at Key Stages 1 and 2, and the other two at Key Stage 2) where data handling was the central component of topic work.

In the Introduction (page 9) the four main stages of a statistical investigation, summarised by the letters **PCAI**, were suggested as a useful structure around which to plan purposeful data handling. In the first two case studies, the teachers concerned used these four stages explicitly as a way of giving structure and purpose to the data-handling work. The final case study, based on a history-focused local study, was carried out in a more exploratory and open-ended way. Here the children were encouraged to give full vent to their natural curiosity about what life might have been like in their town over 100 years ago. They were able to use all of their senses (including hearing, touch and smell!) in order to collect data from another time.

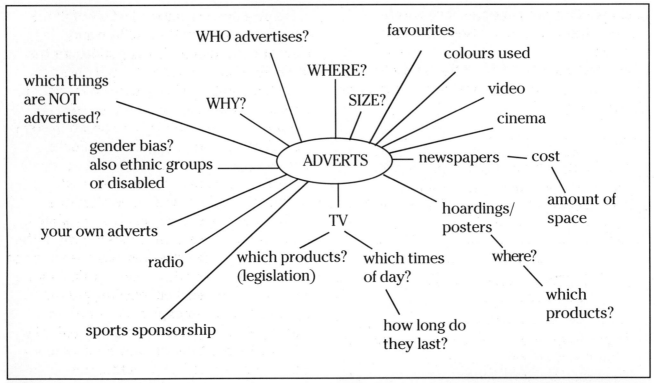

Figure 1

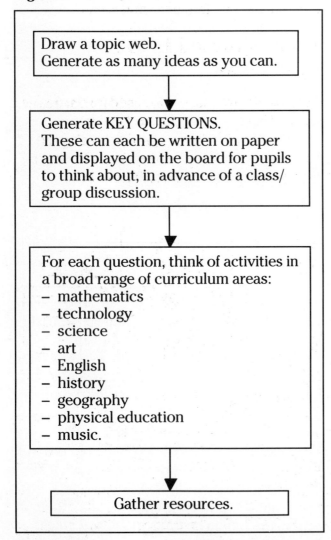

Draw a topic web.
Generate as many ideas as you can.

↓

Generate KEY QUESTIONS.
These can each be written on paper
and displayed on the board for pupils
to think about, in advance of a class/
group discussion.

↓

For each question, think of activities in
a broad range of curriculum areas:
– mathematics
– technology
– science
– art
– English
– history
– geography
– physical education
– music.

↓

Gather resources.

Figure 2

Case study 1

Data handling within the topic 'Advertising' (Key Stage 1)

This case study describes how two teachers from the same school (one with Year 2 pupils and the other with Year 6) worked together on the topic of 'Advertising'. For reasons of space, we have chosen to focus particularly on the Year 2 pupils, but it is important to stress how valuable this collaboration was, particularly for the two teachers involved but also for the two classes of children.

Planning by the teachers in advance

The two teachers decided to plan their work together. As part of their joint preparation, they tried to generate as many ideas as they could, in order to inspire their pupils at Stage **P** (Posing questions) of the **PCAI** cycle.

The topic web which they produced is presented in Figure 1. It shows ideas which the teachers felt could be followed up with data handling work and the flowchart in Figure 2 shows the processes they went through.

The next stage was to get the pupils to pose their own questions. The teachers' strategy is shown in Figure 3.

Start with children discussing ideas in small groups. Questions written on pieces of paper displayed on the wall may spark off ideas.

↓

Whole class discussion.

↓

Pupils to generate their own questions. (Some may choose from those suggested by the teacher.)

↓

Plan the COLLECTING DATA stage. What information will you need to answer your questions?

↓

Gather resources.

Figure 3

Figure 4 overleaf shows just six of the 19 questions posed by the children and teachers, together with suggestions for the possible techniques (graphs and diagrams, etc.) that pupils are likely to need in order to collect and analyse their data successfully.

Some of the questions were posed by Year 2 children, and some by Year 6 children. The two year groups worked on the project separately, but shared their ideas and findings throughout their investigations.

The nature of these questions shows that the children are searching for patterns in the data. However, the class discussions were not merely concerned with collecting data for its own sake. Both teachers encouraged the children to look for explanations for the patterns that they uncovered. *Why* did they think that sweet adverts were shorter than adverts for cars? *Why* was it that the computer adverts largely featured boys and men rather than females? And so on.

How it worked in the classrooms

Each of the two classes focused on particular (and different) questions and chose techniques for collecting and analysing data which they felt to be appropriate. Obviously, many other questions could have been

Posing questions on the topic 'Advertising'

Questions posed	Possible techniques	NC level
1. Which toys are advertised picturing:	mapping diagram	1
girls only;	data collection sheet	2
boys only;	block graph	2
girls and boys.	bar chart	3
	pie chart	5
2. During which programmes (or at what	mapping diagram	1
times) are toys advertised on TV?	data collection sheet	2
	block graph	2
3. How long do certain TV adverts last,	data collection sheet	2, 5
for example those for toys, sweets, food,	continuous data	5
electrical goods, perfume?	mean, median, mode, range	4
Which is the longest/shortest TV advert?	database cards	3
What is a typical length? Do they vary with	computer database	4
time of day?		
4. How much space is used for adverts in a	data collection sheet	2
magazine or newspaper?	measuring area	4
What percentage of the publication is this?	pie charts	5
What are the most common products?		
5. Which products are advertised on: buses,	data collection sheet	2
bus shelters, trains, hoardings?	bar graphs	3
6. Are different racial groups represented in	data collection sheet	2, 5
adverts at different times (within and between	simple percentages	4
which TV programmes do they mostly occur?)		

Figure 4

generated. The questions the children chose led them to use particular techniques, but other investigations would have caused them to draw on different techniques.

For the remainder of this case study we focus mainly on the Year 2 class and describe how the children worked through the **PCAI** process for this topic.

Stage P – Posing the question
(For Year 2 class)

There was a class discussion at the beginning of the project during which pupils talked about the questions they wished to investigate. One aspect which they chose to look at specifically was *toy* advertisements,

and two of the aspects they considered here
were:

1. Do advertisers target their advertising of
   some toys specifically towards girls, and
   others specifically towards boys?
   – Which toys are these?
   – What do you expect to find?
   – After collecting information, were the
     adverts as you expected?

2. How much space is used for toy
   advertisements in
   a) newspapers b) magazines c) comics?
   – What do you expect to find?
   – After investigating, were your results as
     you expected?
   (The children subsequently measured the
   space or area of each advert by covering it
   with Multilink cubes and counting how
   many cubes were needed.)

As can be seen from these questions, a
general strategy used by this Year 2 teacher
was to encourage the pupils to say in advance
what they expected to find, and then, after
carrying out their investigation, to consider
whether their expectations were correct.
This is a useful and motivating learning
strategy, not least because each learner has
a personal investment in the outcome.

Much of the work done by these pupils at
this and later stages was oral. Pupils needed
help from the teacher when recording their
predictions and results. They discussed what
an advertisement was and where they would
find advertisements. To answer these
questions, they decided to search through the
local paper and cut out anything which they
thought was an advertisement. They then
discussed whether or not the clippings were
in fact trying to persuade them to buy an
article or just giving local information.

Next, with greater awareness of what an
advertisement was, the children posed the
following questions:

1. What areas could we sort into? (They
   discussed general categories into which
   they could sort the advert – toys, cars,
   clothes and so on.)

2. Since it was nearing Christmas would there
   be lots of adverts for toys?
3. What different types of printed materials
   may contain adverts?
4. How much space is taken by adverts?
5. Which toys would direct their advertising
   to boys only, girls only or both?
6. Could we predict what we would find out
   before we collected the data?

Stage C – Collecting the data

(For Year 2 Class)
Next the children had to decide which data
needed to be collected to answer the
questions posed.

Once the main questions were agreed, the
children formed into working groups in order
to collect and process the data. A major
decision which affected all the groups was

17

how to decide on the different categories of adverts. After some discussion the children settled on the following categories:

Toys	Entertainment
House and electrical	Cars
Food/Drink	Holidays
Money	Medical
Perfume/Jewellery	Clothes
Other	

One group of children decided to look at which products were given the most and least advertising space in newspapers and magazines. Before they started to collect any data, they discussed their predictions with their teacher.

Another group of children was interested to find out which toys were advertised in comics using:

a) girls only in the picture;
b) boys only in the picture;
c) both girls and boys in the picture.

While the pupils' representation was highly imaginative, it was actually rather difficult for someone else to make sense of. The teacher's own summary of the children's predictions

(as shown in Figure 5) looked rather different. It shows how each of the four children, Emma, Peter, James and Sally, thought the categories would be aimed: at girls only (G); boys only (B); or both girls and boys (G/B).

	Emma	Peter	James	Sally
Toys	B	B		B
Entertainment				
House/Electrical				
Cars			B	
Food/Drink	G/B	G/B	G/B	
Holidays			G/B	
Money		G	G	
Medical				
Perfume/Jewellery	G			G
Clothes				
Other				

Figure 5: Teacher's summary of the children's predictions.

18

Stage A – Analysing the data

(For Year 2 Class)
Shown in the format of the teacher's table (Figure 5), the predictions revealed some interesting patterns. Why, for example, did the two boys not recognise that Perfume/Jewellery advertisements might have been aimed at girls? Did they read all the way to the bottom of the list, or did they run out of steam after reaching the 'Money' category? It remains unclear whether the children deliberately chose not to complete their analysis of particular categories of advertisements.

Here is the teacher's account of the children's work at this stage:

'The children used a BBC computer and the NCET's simple database program *OURFACTS* to produce graphs. *Grasshopper* was available but was too complex for children of this age. Although the children chose their own categories to sort the adverts into, they did not design their own data collection sheet as they had had little experience of such in Year 1 so I did this for them (see Figure 6).'

The children were able to draw a variety of helpful graphs using the computer.

Stage I – Interpreting the results

(For Year 2 and Year 6 classes)
As the various investigations reached their final stage, the children tried to decide who had predicted each result. They compared their findings with their earlier predictions and, where the results were very different, tried to explain why this difference might have occurred.

The graphs that were drawn in stage **A** were examined and the children tried to draw

	Magazine	Number of adverts
Toys		
Entertainment		
House and Electrical		
Cars		
Food/Drink		
Holidays		
Money		
Medical		
Perfume/Jewellery		
Clothes		
Other		

Figure 6: Data collection sheet devised by teacher.

conclusions from them. These conclusions were mainly brought out in discussion. Throughout each discussion, the teachers kept reminding the children to focus on how their interpretation of the graphs was helping them to answer their original questions. In general, this meant moving from making statements like 'This is the tallest bar' to something more useful such as 'The graph shows that there were more food and drink adverts than any other type of advert'.

After looking at the children's work, one or two points were made by the teachers.

(i) It was not always clear what each child was trying to find out. It proved extremely helpful if the questions and predictions could be written down at the beginning.

(ii) Although the results and graphs were often clearly presented (stage **A** of the **PCAI** cycle), the children from both classes were unwilling to write their conclusions down. However, if the original question posed was written at the top of the work, pupils could be encouraged to think about the answer to that question.

A common feature of the data handling work done by these pupils (indeed, by pupils and students of all ages) was their lack of conclusions. Pupils frequently needed to be reminded to think about and write down what they had found out. If they started with a question clearly in mind, then conclusions and interpretation of results seemed to follow on from this without too much difficulty. All too frequently though, they would arrive at a numerical answer (an average, say) or a table or graph and be willing to stop there, rather than take their work on to the final stage of saying or writing down what they had found out about the question they were investigating. Experience suggests that the teacher's role is vital in encouraging the children to follow through the cycle to the end. Without this support, children easily lose sight of the original question which is driving the investigation and there is a danger of the whole enterprise simply petering out.

One simple but effective strategy is to ask the children to write their central question on a large poster and stick it up on the wall as a constant reminder of what they are doing and why. Another is for the teacher to try to build in a response at the end of the project so that the pupils feel that they are working towards something concrete – in this case, perhaps a letter to the Advertising Standards Authority on the subject of sexism in advertising (Year 6), or a presentation of their findings to another class, to the whole school or to interested parties (Year 2).

Case study 2

Data handling within the topic 'Communication' (Key Stage 2)

This investigation was carried out with a group of 27 Year 6 children of mixed ability within the general topic 'Communication'. The class had little, if any, experience of carrying out an enquiry-based approach to learning, so this way of working was very new to them. As with the previous case study, the teacher used the **PCAI** cycle explicitly to help the pupils organise their thinking and to structure and plan their written work. A particular feature of this case study was

that the pupils were not willing to abandon their investigation when the original question had been answered. Instead, they were inspired to pose a second question for investigation and so went through the entire **PCAI** cycle twice.

Stage P – Posing the question (1)

The investigation began with a class discussion on letters and how they get from one person to another. The first question the teacher asked the class was 'What do you need, to send a letter?'

Such a question appeared to pose little or no problem for them – they knew that a letter needs to be properly addressed and to have a postage stamp on it. The teacher then asked what sort of stamps could be put on letters, and this question proved not so straightforward. A number of the children realised that there were first- and second-class stamps, but some went on to suggest there were third-class stamps. There was also uncertainty as to the cost of first- and second-class stamps for an ordinary letter. A number of the children knew roughly how much they cost, suggesting a variety of prices around the correct amounts. At this point the class consulted a leaflet on 'UK Letter Rates', which their teacher had obtained from the Post Office, to confirm the actual prices.

When asked why a first-class stamp should cost more, the class came up with two possible theories. Some thought that the cost was related to the distance travelled by the letter, while others felt that you paid extra for the speed with which it got there ('it got there quicker'). On looking at the leaflet again they realised that as long as the letter was sent somewhere in the UK, either a first- or second-class stamp could be used. This eliminated the first of their theories.

Thus the class had established that a first-class stamp costs more because it is intended to get the letter to its destination more quickly. With a little encouragement from their teacher, the children then agreed on the wording of the first question to be investigated:

'*Do* first-class letters get to their destination more quickly than second-class letters?'

Stage C – Collecting the data (1)

On being asked how they could test their question, one child suggested that they could send two letters to the same place at the same time (one having a first-class stamp and the other a second-class stamp) and see which got there more quickly. The children decided to carry out this test.

After some input from their teacher they also realised that they could collect information from the letters received in their homes, and use this information to see whether or not first-class letters do get to their destinations more quickly. Many of the children, when it was mentioned, seemed aware of the information in red circles on envelopes (the frank marks from the Post Office), but had not thought of using this information until prompted.

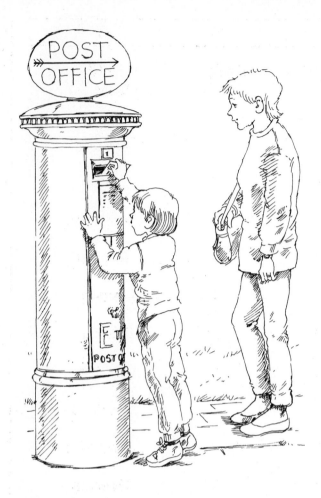

Stage A – Analysing the data (1)

Although not every child collected data from letters received at home, enough were brought in to provide a reasonably large sample. They typed the information into the spreadsheet *Grasshopper*, and the teacher showed them how to enter a formula on to the spreadsheet to calculate how many days each letter took to arrive. This was the children's first experience of using a spreadsheet, so it was done step by step in front of the whole class on the large monitor. Part of the spreadsheet, along with the formula used, is reproduced in Figure 8. The formula worked because all the dates were within one calendar month and did not cross into a second month. If they had spanned two different months, this formula would not have been correct. For example, if a letter was sent on the 31st of one month and received on the 2nd of the next month, the formula would give -29 $(2 - 31 = -29)$.

Note: Figures 8, 9 and 10 show extracts from the spreadsheets that the children used. Where appropriate, the formulas for particular cells have been added. For those who aren't sure how these formulas have been arrived at, they are explained in the appendix at the end of this chapter.

The next question to be addressed was what information they needed to collect. The children realised that they needed to know whether the letter was sent first- or second-class and how long it took to arrive. They also suggested that they needed to know where it had been sent from. It did not seem immediately apparent to the class that to work out how long the letter took they needed to know when it was sent and when it arrived, but this was clarified in discussion.

The next stage was to draw up a data sheet which could be taken home to collect the information. As the children had had little or no experience of this, it was done as a class activity. An example of the data sheet is shown in Figure 7.

Altogether there was information on 40 letters – 13 first-class and 27 second-class. The teacher asked the children whether they thought this difference between the number in each category would cause difficulties. After some discussion, the children decided this would make the test unfair. They said that to be fair there had to be an equal number in each, so it was decided to use all the first-class letters and the 'first' 13 second-class letters brought into the classroom. (In the event, this selection process was not

Stamp (cost)	Date sent	Date received	Where sent from	Time taken

Figure 7: The data sheet devised.

:	A	B	C	D	E
00	STAMP COST	DATE SENT	RECEIVED	DAYS TAKEN	WHERE FROM
01	24	20	21	1	London
02	24	16	18	2	London
03	18	15	18	3	Newcastle
04	18	15	18	3	Newcastle
05	24	18	19	1	London
06	18	28	30	2	Chester
07	18	4	6	2	Chester
08	18	15	16	1	Romford
09	18	15	19	4	North'ton
10	18	12	14	2	S Shields
11	18	8	11	3	S Shields
12	18	11	19	8	Swindon

Formula for cell D01: C01 - B01

Figure 8: Part of the initial spreadsheet.

A	B	C	D	E	F	G	H	I	J	K
00:					DAYS TAKEN					
01:	1	2	3	4	5	6	7	8	TOTAL DAYS	AVERAGE
02: 1st Class	10	2	1	0	0	0	0	0	17	1.31
03: 2nd Class	1	5	5	1	0	0	0	1	38	2.92

Formula for cell J02: B01 *B02 + C01 *C02 + D01 *D02

Formula for cell K02: J02/(B02 + C02 + D02)

Figure 9: Spreadsheet showing average time taken by letters.

Stage I – Interpreting the data (1)

The class then set about investigating what the results showed. During stage **C** of the investigation, before the averages were calculated, a number of the children had already expressed the belief that first-class letters got to their destinations more quickly. Their reasoning was that most of the first-class letters appeared to get to their destination after one day, whereas only one second-class letter got to its destination after one day (most of them taking either two or three days). The averages backed this up, showing it took an average of 1.31 days to deliver a first-class letter and 2.92 days to deliver a second-class letter. This was then compared with the 'UK Letter Rates' leaflet, which stated 'The Royal Mail aims to deliver… first-class letters the day after collection'. The results the children came up with seemed to indicate that the Royal Mail was all but achieving this aim. It was noted, however, that there was one unusual letter in the second-class sample. This was the letter that took eight days to arrive. The children recognised that this extremely untypical value was likely to have a big effect on the second-class average. They recalculated the second-class average, ignoring this unusual value, and found that, although lower, it was still more than the first-class average.

Stage P – Posing the question (2)

Having appeared to have answered their initial question, the children still wanted to pursue the question of the link between distance and how long it took a letter to be delivered. The second question that they decided to investigate was worded as follows:

'Does it take longer to deliver letters that travel a long way than letters that travel only a short way?'

Stage C – Collecting the data (2)

In order to answer this question it was necessary to collect some new data. Most of the data were already there – where the letters came from and how long they took to get to their destination. However, they did need to work out the distance from where

strictly necessary since the averages that they calculated did not need to be based on equal sample sizes. However, the teacher decided to let the children proceed with their method and sensibly chose not to raise this point.

The information from both categories was tabulated to show how many first-class letters took one day, two days, and so on. Everybody in the class was given the opportunity of doing this on paper as the teacher thought it was an important experience. This was keyed into the spreadsheet (Figure 9) and the spreadsheet was used to work out the average time taken to deliver both first- and second-class letters. However, before the children calculated averages, their teacher spent time with them clarifying what averages were and how they were calculated.

	A	B	C	D	E	F	G	H	I	J	K
00:					DAYS TAKEN						
01:	1st CLASS	1	2	3	4	5	6	7	8	TOTAL	AVERAGE
02:										DAYS	DAYS
03:	0-100	5	0	0	0	0	0	0	0	5	1
04:	101-200	2	1	0	0	0	0	0	0	4	1.33
05:	201-300	3	1	1	0	0	0	0	0	8	1.6
06:											
07:											
08:	2nd CLASS	1	2	3	4	5	6	7	8	TOTAL	AVERAGE
09:										DAYS	DAYS
10:	0-100	0	3	5	0	0	0	0	0	21	2.63
11:	101-200	0	2	0	1	0	0	0	0	8	2.67
12:	201-300	1	0	0	0	0	0	0	1	9	4.5

Formula for cell K05 (average): J05/(B05+C05+D05)

Figure 10: Spreadsheet showing average delivery times in the distance bands.

each letter was sent and its final destination. This was done using atlases, and followed on nicely from work the children had been doing on maps and scale.

Stage A – Analysing the data (2)

All this information was then tabulated, with the distances placed in three bands: 0–100 miles, 101–200 miles and 201–300 miles. The children produced a final table showing how long the letters in these bands took to get to their destinations. This information was put into the spreadsheet and again they used the spreadsheet program to calculate averages and draw (or display) helpful graphs, as shown in Figures 10 and 11.

Stage I – Interpreting the data (2)

The averages calculated in the table for distances, and indeed the graphs, seemed to show quite clearly that the further a letter had to go, the longer it took. However, for the first-class letters the time taken only went up marginally. The table also showed that for all

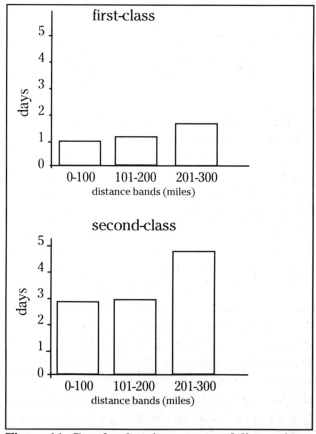

Figure 11: Graphs showing average delivery time

three categories of distance, first-class letters still got there more quickly than second-class letters in the shortest distance band. The class seemed to think that the graphs showed this better than the table, presenting it in a much clearer manner. At this point the teacher suggested that they might like to send a letter to the Post Office telling them what they had learned. This idea was enthusiastically received, so two children set about writing a letter which was duly sent.

Throughout the investigation, the pupils worked in small groups. As a concluding activity, each group was given copies of all the results produced by the entire class and was asked to discuss what they thought had been found out. Each group then reported back to the whole class. Part of the subsequent class discussion involved identifying the main weaknesses of these findings. It seemed obvious to some of the children, based on tests carried out in science lessons, that they had used only a small sample, and therefore the results might not be as accurate as those from a bigger sample. As one pupil commented, 'Since it was only a small sample, the eight day second-class letter could have had a 'bad' effect on our results.'

Capturing the imagination

A class of Year 5 children was divided into groups and walked along Market Place, Willenhall, West Midlands. They recorded impressions of sounds and sights, and tried to record the names and types of shop on a simple tally sheet and on large-scale street maps. The intention was to spend a morning on this survey. However, at 10.30 am it poured with rain and the class had to shelter under the canopy of a butcher's shop. When the rain stopped, they retraced their steps, this time avoiding the pedestrianised precinct and walking through the Victorian alley-ways and side-streets hidden behind the modern façades.

These parts of the town were rarely visited. In these alley-ways, the children were able to travel back in time. Their teacher encouraged them to think about the following question:

'What was it like to visit the market place 100 years ago?'

The children listened to water dripping down cast iron pipes, saw rusting grills and boot scrapers. They were surrounded by the aromas of damp slate, bricks, mouldering vegetables, soot and ferns growing out of cracks in the wall. There was a sign 'Court 1' which was barely visible and a few cobblestones were poking out of the mud. Yet in the background, traders in the modern market still cried out as they would have done 100 years ago.

What has all this to do with data handling? The class teacher was trying to give a human face to the children's historical investigation. Back in the classroom they were provided with collections of census returns, trade directories, newspapers, photographs and so on. Their teacher wanted them to remember that the facts, numbers and data that they might be collecting and analysing were about real people.

The children returned to Market Place time and again to gather more impressions and information, always trying to place them in historical context and compare them to the modern day. The teacher worked hard throughout the project to create and maintain a strong emotional appeal for the children by highlighting the importance of the people involved. Nowhere was this more successfully achieved than in their work with Census records from 1881. An extract from the 1881 Census schedule is shown on page 28. A great deal of data was collected about family size, ages, occupations and so on. This information had to be explained, interpreted and the implications considered in order for the children to build up a picture of family life 100 years ago. A lot of detective work followed, looking for clues and piecing them together. Some of the issues which the teacher raised with the class were as follows:

– What questions do we wish to ask?
– What information do we need?
– How can this information be sorted?
– How can it be recorded?
– How can it be displayed?
– Have we used the information to answer our question?
– Can we make a good case for our conclusions?

The children, after interpreting the data, were asked to put forward and provide the reasoning behind an answer for a number of questions. For example:

– Which is the poorest area of Market Place?
– How can you tell?
– Can it be proved using Census records?
– Are there general ways of proving or disproving this sort of question?

The teacher then asked each group of children to identify with a particular family. For example, one group chose as follows: 1881 Census, John Turtin, 33 Market Place.

From the Census, the children knew where John Turtin lived, where and when he was born and some details about his family. What else could they find out and how? A class discussion generated a host of further questions to explore:

– What happened to John Turtin after 1881?
– Was he typical of the Victorian period?
– Can you find a photograph of him or one of his descendants?
– What happened to his family?
– What did his family eat?
– How did his family dress?

John Turtin was represented by a mark on the children's graph, but now he was also a real person for them.

To end this case study, here are the sources of historical data that were used in this project:

– Census records;
– probate records;
– parish records – births, marriages and deaths;
– industrial and trade directories;
– newspapers;
– court records;
– school log books;
– district health records;
– electoral rolls.

The use of local history records enabled these pupils to see the value of collecting data, in order to discuss, interpret and draw conclusions. There was a strong 'speaking

WALSALL LIBRARY & MUSEUM SERVICES - EXTRACT FROM THE 1881 CENSUS SCHEDULE
The originals are in manuscript.

Parish/Township	Borough	Town	Village	Ecclesiastical District	Ref. no.
Walsall Foreign	Walsall	Walsall		St Johns	RG11/2823 p95 rev

NAME OF STREET (with house number)	NAME of each person living there	RELATION to head of Family	Marital Status	AGE M	AGE F	Profession	Where born
7 Queen Street	William Dixon	Head	Married	27		Baker	Hopton, Staffs
	Mary Ann, Dixon	Wife	Married		20		Netherton, Worc
	Florence	Daughter			1		Walsall, Staffs
7A Queen Street	Elizabeth Grainger	Head	Married		46	Housekeeper	Netherton, Worc
	John, "	Son	Unmarried	27		Engineer at Ironworks	W Bromwich
	Samuel, "	Son	Unmarried	17		?	"
	Noah, "	Son	Unmarried	14		Straitener at Ironworks	"
	Sarah "	Daughter			12	Scholar	"
8 Queen Street	James Birch	Head	Married	56		House Painter	Birmingham
	Charlotte Birch	Wife	Married		53		Wednesbury
	John Joseph Birch	Son	Unmarried	16		Cigar Case Maker	Stafford
	Annie Atkinson	Adopted Child			9	Scholar	Stafford
9 Queen Street	Thomas Winn	Head	Married	47		Bricklayer Labourer	Galloway, Ireland
	Annie	Wife	Married		38		Dudley, Worc
	Catherine	Daughter	Unmarried		18	Brush Drawer	Greatbridge, Staffs
	Mary Ellen	Daughter	Unmarried		16	Tailoress	Walsall, Staffs
	John	Son		14		Brush Drawer	Greatbridge, Staff
	Honour	Daughter			6	Scholar	"
	Owen	Son		2			"
	William Thomas Williams	Grandson	Unmarried	5			"
	William Bradley	Visitor	Unmarried	50		Shoe Maker	Bromyard, Hereford

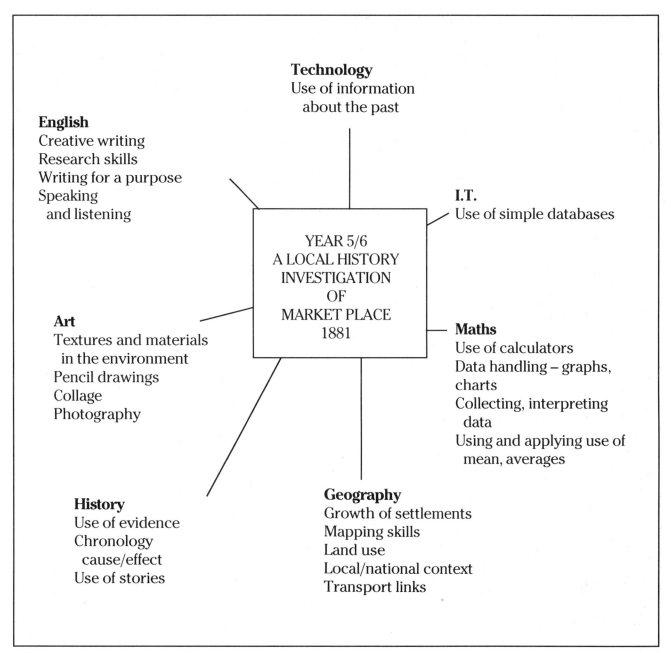

Figure 12: A topic web for history work.

and listening' component, especially when the children were talking about forms of representation which may have been new to them, such as bar and line graphs, pie charts, frequency tables and so on. At the end of the project the teacher reflected on the range of skills drawn from across the curriculum which had been used in the children's work. These are summarised on the topic web in Figure 12.

Finally, although this project was not explicitly structured using the **PCAI** model, all four of its elements were clearly evident at different stages of the children's work.

The importance of stage P

This chapter has described ways in which data handling can be made a natural part of the topic work that many schools already carry out. What is highlighted here is the importance of posing a clear question as a way of giving purpose and direction to the data handling activities. Including stage **P** may require only a small adjustment to what many teachers are already doing in project work, but experience suggests that it is a crucially important one.

Appendix

The case studies in this chapter have highlighted the role of the spreadsheet as a way of recording and analysing data. For those who are unfamiliar with interpreting a spreadsheet formula, here is an explanation of the formulas listed in the second case study (Figure 8).

Formula for cell D01:
C01 – B01
The number of days taken for the letter to be delivered is calculated by subtracting the date sent (the value in cell B01) from the date received (the value in cell C01). Once this instruction (C01 – B01) has been entered into cell D01, the formula can be copied down all of the other cells in column D. On a spreadsheet, the copying of a formula can be achieved using a simple instruction and this procedure is often referred to as 'replication'.

Figure 9:
Formula for cell J02:
B01*B02 + C01*C02 + D01*D02
Formula for cell K02:
J02 / (B02 + C02 + D02)

The formula in cell J02 calculates the total number of days that these 13 first-class letters were in transit. Since the number of first-class letters taking one day was ten, the number taking two days was two and the number taking three days was one, the calculation is:

1x10 + 2x2 + 3x1.

Notice that, on a spreadsheet, the symbol for multiplication is '*'. The formula for cell K02 calculates the average number of days taken by the first-class letters. This is the total number of days (the value in cell J02) divided by the total number of first-class letters (the sum of cell values B02, C02 and D02).

Figure 10:
Formula for cell K05 (average):
J05 / (B05 + C05 + D05)
The calculation for this average is identical in principle to that of cell J02 in Figure 3 (described above).
Note: the formulas used in this example are not necessarily the most efficient but happened to be the ones used by this class.

Chapter Two
Collecting data

Data and information

Data is the term used for known facts – often numbers. The purpose of data handling is to extract information from the data or convert the data into a usable form in order to help answer a question.

The key to success in data handling at school is to remember that data must be in a context, and collecting data should have a purpose and must be planned in advance. Pose the question, clarify it, ask what data are needed to answer the question, and then ask what the source of the data will be (survey, experiment, publications...) and how the data are to be obtained and recorded. Secondary data (data already collected by others) can be very useful and should not necessarily be

considered 'second best'. The source does not have to be a heavy HMSO publication – it might be last year's class register, cereal packets brought in by the children (with information about the nutritional value of the contents), sets of stickers or tea cards, the sports pages of local or national papers – in fact any source where data have been collected for use by others.

Collecting data and recording data cannot always be separated. Inevitably this chapter will overlap with the following chapters on analysing data since recording data and analysing data also overlap. By way of introduction we take up the idea mentioned in the introduction, namely that reception children are fascinated with the teacher filling in the register.

Making data handling an everyday event

If the teacher has reservations over data handling, then children cannot be expected fully to appreciate the potential of this topic. In the daily classroom routine there are many possibilities for exposing children to the collection, recording, interpretation and *use* of data. Infant children's interest in the register can be exploited by using a large piece of card covered with clear sticky plastic as a large-scale version of the register, on show to the class (Figure 1).

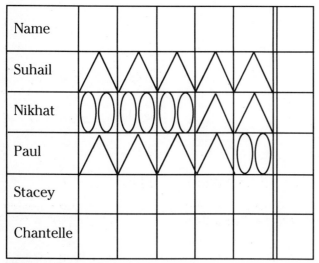

Figure 1

– What do the lines mean?
– What do the ovals mean?
– Why are they this shape?
– Do you think we could make it more interesting? How?

Name						
Suhail						
Nikhat						
Paul						
Stacey						

Figure 2

– How many children are at school today?
– How many all together?
– How many children in a week?
– Is this more or less than last week?
– Do you think there will be more or less children present tomorrow?
– What are the chances of everyone being present tomorrow?

It is worth mentioning here that, while the happy/sad faces are intuitively easier to understand than the lines and ovals (although some pupils might be smiling at the prospect of being absent from school!) it is harder to see overall patterns using this method.

School dinners provide another familiar context for data handling. In many schools children are allowed to choose each Monday what they will eat each day that week. This can be linked with investigating which meals are popular (children's responses may be influenced by the week's menu currently on display).

Data collection based on sorting

Level 1

Programmes of study

'• Selecting criteria for sorting a set of objects and applying them consistently.'
'• recording with objects or drawing and commenting on the results.'

Statement of attainment

'Sort a set of objects, describing the criteria chosen.'

Selecting or sorting objects according to some criterion (or criteria) can be viewed as simple data handling. The objects could be almost anything – buttons, toy cars, dolls, stamps, shoes, children, etc. The criteria for sorting will need to be appropriate for the objects and for the purpose of doing the sorting. The sorting may involve collecting together in a group all those with some particular property (for example blue, over 1cm long, weighing less than 1kg, pupils with fewer than two brothers or sisters) in which case all the remainder form a second group (the 'not...' group). Alternatively, the sorting may involve making several groups, according to the chosen criterion (for example by colour, by month of the year, by transport category – bus, car, bicycle).

Example 1

The teacher placed a bowl of various fruits on the table and asked Natalie 'What fruits are there?' Natalie took the pieces of fruit, one by one, and arranged them on a prepared A3 sheet of paper to form a real-object graph (Figure 3).

This is at one and the same time collecting, sorting and displaying data. It provides the basis for answering the teacher's question and supplementary questions such as:

– Which fruit is there most of?
– Are there more bananas than pears?

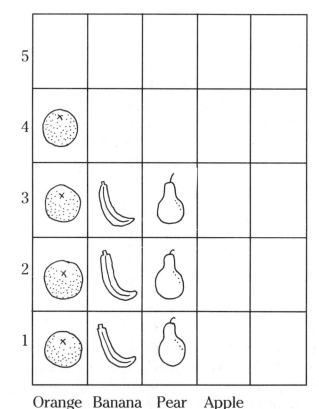

Orange Banana Pear Apple

Figure 3: Fruit in bowl.

– How many apples are there?
– Are there fewer apples than pears?

Example 2

A cloth bag was prepared containing a large number of red counters (25) and white counters (50). The teacher mixed up the counters and asked Amit to tell her something about the contents of the bag by taking out

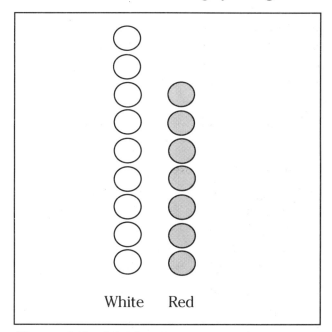

White   Red

Figure 4: Amit's chart.

some counters. Amit gleefully grabbed a handful of counters and created a real-object graph (Figure 4).

The conversation went:
'There are red counters and white counters!'
'And what about other colours?'
'There aren't any.'
'Are you sure?'
'Yes ... no ...'
and so on.

In this example an advanced concept (sampling) is available in the context of a simple sorting exercise – laying the foundation for future statistical work. It can be alluded to at a gentle conversational level: 'We didn't get the same as last time...', etc.

Amit's chart can be used for mapping work – matching one white with one red and finding a surplus of white. This can also link with conservation work: 'If the counters are moved or spread out, are there still as many?'

Work at a higher level can return to such a situation and proceed further:
'Are there more red counters or more white counters in the bag?'
'There are more white counters.'
'Are you sure?'
'Yes ... no ...'
and so on.

Amit's chart could be interpreted as indicating something about the probability of getting white or red. Thus other work at a higher level might proceed:
'If you take out one more counter, which colour is it more likely to be?'
'Why?'
'If you take out ten more counters, which colour will there be more of?'
and so on.

Experiments should follow to see what actually happens and to promote further discussion. This should focus on the *variability* of the results and on *predictability*, which increases with a larger number of trials (that is, picking a counter, then another, then another...) or with taking a larger sample (that is, taking a handful).

Example 3

The children themselves can be the data which are collected! The teacher asks the class 'Are there more children wearing dark coloured shoes or more wearing light coloured shoes?' The children line up to answer this (Figure 5).

Figure 5: Children lining up according to shoe colour.

Example 4

The teacher (or class, working with prepared materials) makes a collection of cloth snakes of a variety of colours, patterns, lengths and thicknesses, and with a variety of eyes and tongues. These can then be used for a host of sorting activities (Figure 6).

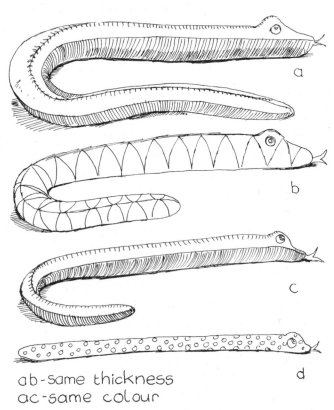

ab-same thickness
ac-same colour

Figure 6: Cloth snakes.

Collecting, sorting and displaying

Collecting data naturally merges into displaying the data through the intermediate step of sorting. At Level 1 the actual collection process is very simple. The first example (fruit) merely requires taking and sorting the fruit. The second example (counters) is actually a sampling activity (Level 4 implicitly – conducting a survey; Level 5 explicitly) but is quite appropriate for very young children, and involves sorting the counters into two groups. The third example (shoes) requires the children to sort themselves into two groups. The fourth example (snakes) can progress from sorting into two groups to sorting into many groups, and from using one criterion to using two or more criteria.

Asking children to sort any set of things into two piles and then asking them why they got what they did gives them the opportunity to think about and describe their criteria.

Sorting activities can provide an introduction to two-way tables (or matrices) where the children place pieces in appropriate positions on a table drawn on the floor or on a large sheet of paper (Figure 7).

	Circle	Square	Triangle	Oblong
Yellow				
Green				

Figure 7: Two-way table

This could be developed into number work using cards showing different numbers of various objects. The cards could be sorted on to a table such as that shown in Figure 8.

Children often have collections of things related to reading – spelling lists, dictionaries, back copies of comics... These could be used for sorting activities at a variety of levels. For example, spelling lists can be classified according to initial letter, number of letters in the word, difficulty and so on.

The theme of sorting is taken up again in Chapter 6 on Databases.

Data collecting as counting and classifying

The first programme of study item is an extension of that in Level 1. Here the child is expected to *choose* criteria rather than *select* the criteria. This is probably intended to be interpreted as choosing the categories rather than choosing the context; *choose* suggests a more open-ended process than *select*.

Example

The class had been studying a photograph of a class of primary school children at the turn of the century. Luke remarked that all the children seemed to be wearing the same colour shoes (black). This led to discussion and prompted the teacher to invite Luke to 'Find out about the colours of our class's shoes', so that a comparison could be made with life long ago. Luke had to decide what colour names to use, which caused some difficulties.

	fewer than 10 things	10 things	more than 10 things
balloons			
sheep			
cars			
other things			

Figure 8

Shoes did not always fit nicely into the standard name categories he knew, and disagreements arose. This led to useful class discussion. (Colours of actual objects can be quite difficult since we can distinguish thousands of colours and have only a very few colour names! An activity about favourite colour would have been a lot easier, but much less instructive.)

How were the data collected?

Luke went round the class interviewing everyone and writing down the information on a piece of paper. He wrote down each child's name plus his own and the teacher's, and next to it the relevant colour. (The teacher might have supplied a class list to help Luke – in effect a data collection sheet. See Figure 9.)

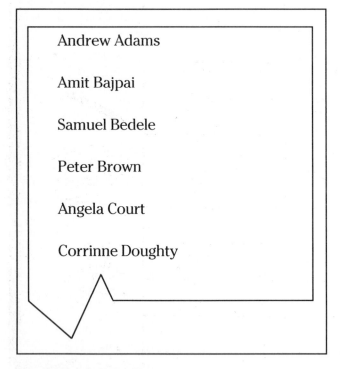

Andrew Adams

Amit Bajpai

Samuel Bedele

Peter Brown

Angela Court

Corrinne Doughty

Figure 9: A class list.

This provides a nice example of a simple data handling question arising naturally out of a day-to-day classroom situation. The teacher chose to 'run with it', and not let the opportunity slip by.

How else might Luke have recorded the data?

A tally chart is another means to record the information (or to analyse it). This is a Level 4 activity, but might be done much earlier if the

circumstances are appropriate. It is standard practice to use a crossed stroke for each fifth entry. The advantage is that it eases counting. However, this assumes that counting in fives can be done. There is also a danger of forgetting to put the fifth stroke in at the correct time. For relatively small numbers, the simpler system of recording all strokes in the same way may be better (see Figure 10). Alternatively, instead of marks on paper, one could place matchsticks in a box and then line them up.

Colour	Number
Black	I I I I I I
Brown	I I I I
White	I
Red	I I I

Figure 10: A simple tally chart.

A good way for children to collect data which involves counting events is to use a calculator:

> set the constant to 'add 1',
> zero the calculator,
> and press '=' to record each event.

Using the constant facility in this way means that one is added to the display each time '=' is pressed. It is advisable to have more than one 'counter' in case of an accident. In fact this also provides an opportunity to talk about errors and accuracy, the need for checking and pooling results.

Figure 11 shows one Key Stage One science activity which can be closely tied to the mathematics Attainment Target 5 Level 2 'choosing criteria to sort and classify objects; recording results or outcomes of events'. After completing the scientific experiment on the worksheet, the children can attempt to sort the objects according to how they behaved with the magnet and be asked to consider what is the same about the group of objects that turned out to be magnetic.

Is it magnetic?

You will need: a bar magnet; the objects named below.

▲ Which things will be attracted to a magnet?
Predict first, then use your magnet to find out if
you were right.

▲ Record your results on the chart below.

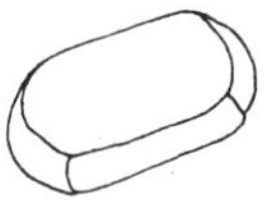

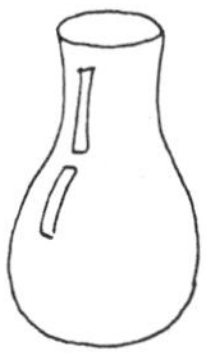

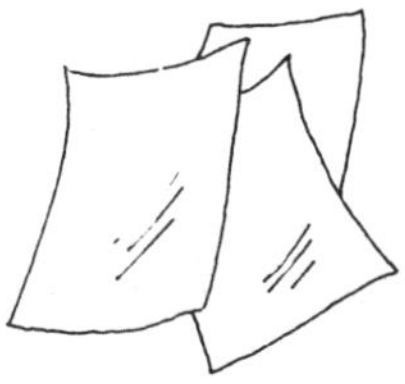

Object	Prediction: will it be magnetic?	Result: is it magnetic?
2p coin		
5p coin		
ruler		
pin		
pencil		
paper-clip		
paper		
foil		
glass jar		
eraser		
bottle top		
nail		
plastic lid		
metal lid		

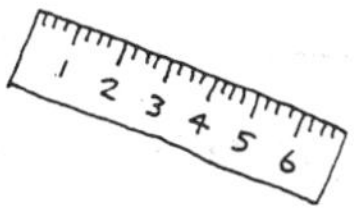

▲ Discuss your results with a friend. What did you find out?

Figure 11: From *Electricity and magnetism* F. Mackay (*Essentials for Science* series, Scholastic).

Collecting data using a simple questionnaire

Class 1 are doing a project on 'Ourselves'. If several items of data are being collected about class members, either all at the same time or over a period, then a questionnaire for each child might be appropriate (see Figure 12).

The questionnaires can either be filled in by each child *or* by an interviewer going round asking the questions and recording the responses. The design of the questionnaire might be the responsibility of one child, a team or the whole class. It can provide inspiration for much discussion. Help from the teacher will be needed – by providing an example and offering advice. A *pilot* interview with the draft questionnaire is recommended – try it out on someone to see if it causes problems through ambiguity, difficulty, failing to cover all cases and so on.

This activity, certainly with quite a number of Year 2 children, can be extended to entry into a computer database such as *DSHOW*, *OURFACTS* or *Junior Pinpoint* – thereby progressing nicely into Level 3 as described in the following.

What is your name? ....

Which class are you in? ....

Do you like school?   Yes/No

Which day do you like most? ....

Tick your favourite subject:

☐   Technology

☐   Science

☐   Mathematics

☐   English

Figure 12: Questionnaire.

Accessing data
The varieties of sources of data

Level 3

Programme of study
'• **extracting specific pieces of information from tables and lists.**'

Statement of attainment
'**Access information in a simple database.**'

Practical statistical work at school has often been limited to collecting data by 'doing surveys using questionnaires'. However, doing experiments and extracting information from existing sources are other valuable approaches. This programme of study draws attention to the value of working with data in tables.

Primary and secondary data

Data collected by the person doing the investigation are called *primary* data. Data taken from existing sources are called *secondary* data. In the past, sources of secondary data have been largely ignored for school statistical work. One reason for this is that, because they are secondary data, the investigator is more detached from the data and the information may be less interesting ('boring statistics'). This is mainly because the work has lacked purpose and been seen as a vehicle for teaching mathematics. The teacher needs to ensure that there is a well-defined and shared purpose in studying the data. A combination of primary and secondary data may be the answer, for example comparing 'Our Class' with last year's class or another school's class or with a class of children from 100 years ago.

A good source of *primary* data is from work in other subject areas such as IT, geography and science. Some examples from Scholastic Publications books in the *Practical Guides* series are given in Chapter 10.

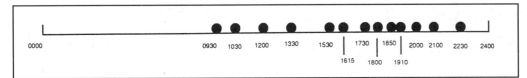

Figure 14: Time line for departures on Sundays.

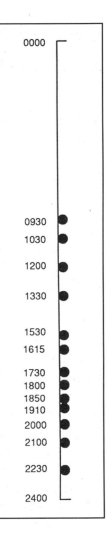

Examples of sources of *secondary* data are timetables, catalogues, weather reports, reference books, computer screens, Ceefax, local telephone directories, Thompson's Guides, sports tables in newspapers, specialist books (science, biology, geography, history...). At the end of this chapter there is a further section devoted to sources of secondary data.

It is better to use original source material rather than doctored versions, but this is often not feasible at Key Stages 1 and 2. Most timetables are too difficult to be used with young children but British Rail produce simple cards (see Figure 13) which might be used with guidance.

Some questions to ask are:
– How many trains go from London to Loughborough on Sundays?
– And on Mondays?
– On which days are there fewest trains?
– When are there most trains? A deliberately vague question!

Pupils might construct a timeline (vertical or horizontal) to help them to answer some of these questions (see Figure 14). This can be used in the same way as a number line, for subtraction (differences between times). Also, it shows the bunching of trains at certain times and the lack of trains late at night and early in the morning. These features can be brought out through questioning – with children asked why the observed patterns occur.

Children are often able to pose their own questions about the timetable, and usually enjoy doing so. The timetable could also be woven into a detective story in which the children are invited to sift through certain evidence and solve a mystery. (*Could* the suspect have been in London station at 9 am and have committed the crime in Loughborough at 10.30 am?)

Using the computer

Information stored in a computer database by some external agency and then interrogated by the class would be an example of working with secondary data.

If the data were collected directly by the class and entered into the database themselves for interrogation, then the data would be primary data.

INTERCITY

London → Loughborough
Principal train service 04 October 1993 to 28 May 1994

Mondays to Fridays				Saturdays	
		London St Pancras depart	Loughborough arrive	London St Pancras depart	Loughborough arrive
✕	▲	0800	0927	0830	1002
✕	▲	0900	1030	1000	1128
		1030	1154	1030	1204
		1200	1327	1145	1311
		1330	1454	1230	1404
		1500	1625	1400	1531
	▼	1600	1727	1530	1705
	▲	1630	1805	1600	1733
A	▲	1715	1845	1700	1832
✕	▲	1800	1924	1730	1906
✕	▲	1850	2022	1915	2054
		2000	2134	2015	2157
		2145	2338	2115	2317
●	fx	2315	0115		
●	fo	2336	0115		

Sundays	
0930	1132
1030	1227
1200	1357
1330	1532
1530	1706
1615	1744
1730	1855
1800	1933
1850	2024
1910	2045
2000	2136
2100	2244
2230	0022

Figure 13: BR timetable

Sometimes computers are used to generate the data. A program can be used to simulate throwing a die:

```
10 REPEAT
20 PRINT RND (6)
30 UNTIL GET$ = "S"
```

This BBC BASIC program produces a sequence of random digits, each a digit from 1 to 6. The user presses any key (spacebar recommended) to get the next digit, or presses 'S' to stop.

Experimental data generated in this way are primary data. This is an example of a simulation.

Many spreadsheets also offer this facility and a simple instruction will produce a long list of random numbers on the screen.

Interrogating a computer database should be seen as an activity for a purpose, and not just as a vacuous exercise to familiarise the pupil with what a database is and how data can be extracted. It should, therefore, begin with a question. The data to answer the question may already reside in the computer. If not they will need to be collected.

Example 1

A database of animals and their habitats is in the computer. The teacher asks 'Which animals live in the sea?' and 'Which animals live in trees?' The pupils turn to the source from which they can collect the data to answer these questions. (See Chapter 6 on Databases.)

Example 2

The teacher suggests the day before sports day that 'boys run faster than girls'. This is discussed, clarified (*all* boys and *all* girls of *all* ages at *all* schools?) and a plan devised to test it. Arrangements are made to collect all the data from sports day, and this is fed into the computer for analysis.

Surveys and censuses

A *survey* is an investigation to collect data from individual members of a group (for example: birds visiting the school pond; children in Class 5; used car adverts in the local paper). If the survey includes *all* the individuals it has the special name of *census*. A census seeks information about the *whole population*. 'Census' is, in practice, mainly restricted to large-scale investigations, for example a traffic census on a major road counting all traffic for a week. If a survey only picks out some of the individuals it is called a *sample survey*. How the sample is chosen is very important but that is an issue mostly beyond Key Stages 1 and 2.

Level 4

Programme of study

'• **specifying an issue for which data are needed.**'

Statement of attainment

'**Conduct a survey on an issue of their choice.**'

These are an ill-matched pair. The programme of study refers to something which is a preliminary to collecting data, but the statement of attainment is about actually collecting data. Both are important, of course.

'Specifying an issue' can mean deciding what the general area of interest is (for example sport), homing in on a particular aspect (such as what sports Class 5 like to watch on TV) and then agreeing on a suitable question (or questions) to find out the information. Using a topic web to put down the class's thoughts can be helpful (see Chapter 1 for an example of this). Another example of a topic web is provided in Figure 15, taken from *Practical Guides: Science* by Graeme Kent (Scholastic Publications Ltd, 1990).

The last three words of the statement of attainment – 'of their choice' – are very important in that they signify that there must be interest and purpose in conducting the survey, and that the children are not carrying it out simply because the teacher says so. The teacher can, of course, have an influence in encouraging particular lines of

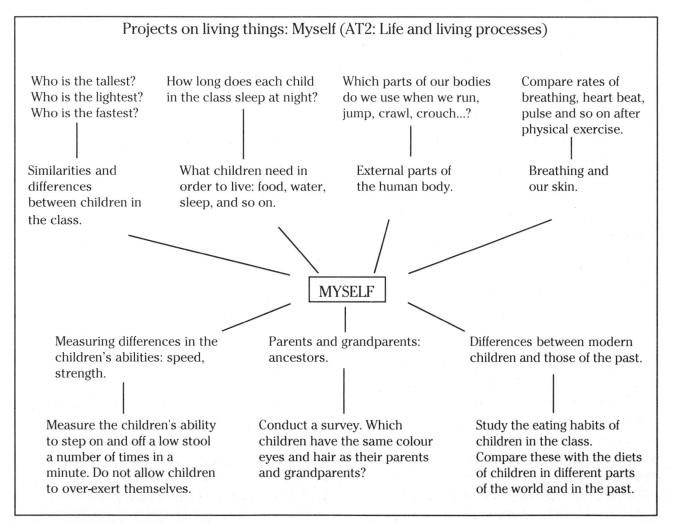

Figure 15: Topic web for science

work and indeed good teachers are able to make the children's choices their own and vice versa.

Example
A class were doing some work on holidays. Individual children wrote to different embassies and received varying amounts of material in response. The competition for 'Who's got the most?' became intense, leading to weighing the packages, counting the pages, counting up the stamps on the packages, measuring the thickness of the paper, and so on, as the children wrestled with just what 'the most' meant. This is another example of choosing to run with a question that arose naturally from the children's work in another context.

Perhaps the best known example of a 'survey' is the national Census of Population which is held every ten years. This aims to count everyone in the country (an impossible task!) and find out about their circumstances and how they conduct their lives. The most recent one was 1991. Public libraries have

masses of data from these censuses, which began in 1881, and from the many other large-scale surveys. For more details see the section on sources of data at the end of this chapter and also Chapter 10.

A census seeks to count every member in a population, whereas a survey is usually based on a representative sample. Further discussion of censuses, surveys and sampling is to be found towards the end of this chapter.

Example
It was election time and conversation in Class 5A came round to polls and their effectiveness in finding out opinions. This led to some practical work on gathering data when there are too many people to ask everyone. Joanne was asked to find out Class 5A's favourite sports by asking a sample of six members of the class. Her reported result did not include any mention of football.

This provided an opportunity for the teacher to ask the class what they thought about Joanne's findings. (Why did football not feature? She only asked her friends and none of them happened to have an interest in football.) This led on, in a simple way, to the idea of a biased sample for which the result is of dubious value.

Collecting, analysing and drawing conclusions – three in one

Level 4

Programme of study
'• collecting, grouping and ordering discrete data using tallying methods...'

At this level it is feasible for children to collect simple data directly into a table in encoded form – the tally chart (Figure 16). This is more sophisticated than writing each piece of information out separately as it is collected. With such a collection/recording system there is a loss of information – it is not known which individual is associated with each individual mark. There is increased possibility of error – putting a mark in the wrong place, for example, and checking is difficult. The advantages are that collecting the data is speedy and the collection, recording and display/analysis processes are merged. The tally chart is a diagram as well as a table and it builds up as the data are collected.

colour	number
black	⫲⫲ ‖
brown	⫲⫲	
white	⫲⫲ ‖|
red	‖|

Figure 16: A tally chart.

The word discrete means that the items are clearly separated, for example there may be 13 woodlice or 14 woodlice but there can't be 13.45 woodlice! Counting leads to discrete data. Usually this involves whole numbers. An exception, for example, is shoe size which is discrete but not restricted to integers: 1, 1 , 2, 2 and so on. On the other hand there are continuous data. For example, if we were actually to measure shoe length, any degree of accuracy would be possible, for instance 16.1234567cm. Continuous data are less easy to represent. These issues are discussed more fully in Chapter 3.

Level 5

Programme of study
'• inserting, and interrogating data in a computer database; drawing conclusions.'

Statement of attainment
'Use a computer database to draw conclusions.'

The emphasis on 'computer database' and 'conclusions' is very proper (drawing conclusions is the subject matter of a separate chapter) but it still needs to be remembered that this all depends on data.
• There are the raw data which have been collected – these have been inserted into the computer database.
• The database is interrogated – this interrogation may be done by those who inserted the data or by others.
• In the process of insertion the data may have been changed in some way. For example, dates of birth may have been coded into ddmmyy format (such as 120988) or even yymmdd (such as 880912) or names may have been abbreviated – this will of course need interpreting when the data are retrieved.
The intervention of the computer makes data collection and data analysis less distinct. Since computer databases can be used to perform simple analysis of data, the

information which comes out may be raw data (such as the heights of individual class members) or derived numerical data (such as the computed average height) or derived graphical data (such as a graph showing the frequencies of heights in categories 'short', 'medium', 'tall'). Gathering this information can be viewed as data collection or as analysis – the distinction is blurred. For example, standing at a vegetable stall in the town market and recording in a tally chart what products each customer buys is both collecting data and a simple form of analysing data.

At this level, analysing and drawing conclusions are also somewhat blurred. If the object is to determine whether the girls in Year 5 wish to be allowed to play football, then a census might be arranged and the yes/no responses recorded directly on a tally sheet. The conclusion might be a simple recognition that the 'yes' line is much longer than the 'no' line, so the girls *do* wish to play football. (The conclusion does have to be made and this is a significant cognitive act. Going beyond this to consider the implications, or questioning the validity of the exercise are appropriate for Key Stages 3 and 4.)

Collecting data on forms – facts and opinions

Forms

Level 5

Programme of study

'• designing and using an observation sheet to collect data; collating and analysing results.'

Statement of attainment

'Design and use an observation sheet to collect data.'

Level 5

Programme of study

'• collecting, ordering and grouping continuous data using equal class intervals and creating frequency tables.'

The above are discussed more fully in Chapters 3 and 4 as they largely relate to the analysis rather than collection of data.

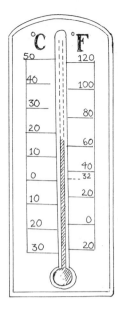

It should be noted that collecting continuous data with perfect accuracy is impossible. Usually the continuous variable (a time, length, mass, temperature) is measured to some accuracy and the continuous data are made discrete. For example, heights are measured to the nearest centimetre, temperatures to the nearest degree Celsius (or Fahrenheit, which is a different level of accuracy). Collecting continuous data is thus a more involved process – questions of accuracy have to be addressed. When there is a large number of categories (height might vary from 90cm to 130cm which is 41 categories) then grouping may be required for display or analysis (90 to 94cm, 95 to 99cm).

The terms 'observation sheet', 'data collection form', 'questionnaire' are often used interchangeably and it is not easy or even worthwhile trying to be too precise. There are so many circumstances and ways for collecting data that terminology cannot be clear-cut. However here are some suggestions:

• An *observation sheet* is a form for recording information which the user observes – such as counting the numbers and types of bird on the local lake. This is factual information rather than opinion.

• More generally, *data collection forms* may be used to collect information by asking people questions. For example car drivers may be stopped at a traffic census and asked to state the purpose of their journey. Again, this is factual information rather than opinion.

• *Questionnaires* are commonly used to survey opinion (and less often to gather factual information). They are met in Level 6, which is described in the next section.

Although there are two separate and different programme of study entries here, there is only one statement of attainment, which is puzzling. There should also be something along the lines: 'Design and use a form to collect factual information.'

Questionnaires are data collection forms with questions to be completed by people. Usually people fill in their own forms, but there may be an interviewer who asks the questions and writes down the answers. Often questionnaires seek people's opinions but they can be used to gain factual information. They can also be used for propaganda purposes or to convey information:

'Did you know that a harpooned whale takes up to five agonising hours to die?' Yes/No

'Do you support whale hunting for profit?' Yes/No

Designing questionnaires is by no means as simple as it seems. (Many students and business people who have cause to use questionnaires find that they do not elicit the information wanted, for various reasons.) It is therefore a useful topic to return to at different stages. Much depends upon what

the target group is and what data are being sought. Some points to consider are:
- Keep the questions simple.
- Keep the questions short.
- Avoid ambiguity.
- Ensure that the question asked will give precisely the answer sought.
- Avoid embarrassment.
- Make sure the question is neutral and does not encourage one particular response (that is, avoid bias).

Answers can take many forms:
- Open-ended (a sentence or two).
- One word (or at most a few).
- Multiple choice.
- Yes/No.
- Likert scale (often Like – Dislike on a scale of 1 to 5).

This is a rich area to explore and experiment with. See the example in Figure 17.

What is your name?...

How old are you?...

What colour is your hair?............................

What colour are your eyes?...........................

Tick your favourite colour: ☐ Red

☐ Blue

☐ Green

☐ Yellow

Do you have school dinners?   Yes/No

How much do you like cabbage? Ring one number:

1	2	3	4	5
Like very much	Like a bit	Neither like nor dislike	Dislike a bit	Really hate

Figure 17: A questionnaire showing a variety of formats for gathering information.

Sampling

We return to the example of a girl who was asked to find out the class's favourite sports. Joanne's *sample* of her six friends (see pages 42 – 43) who were supposed to reflect the views of the whole class was *not representative* of the total *population* (in this case all of Class 5A). The words in italics are technical terms although borrowed from ordinary English with fairly obvious meaning. The word 'population', however, needs special mention. We associate the word with humans or, at a push, with animals. However, statisticians apply it to any well-defined group: drawing pins in a packet, light bulbs produced by Osram in 1944, fleas on the caretaker's dog, plants growing in the meadow next to the school.

There will always be problems with samples. Their purpose is to find out something about the whole population without the effort of considering every member of the population. And you can't get something for nothing. What results is uncertainty or error, even if there is no obvious bias in the sampling process. These concepts are largely matters for secondary school work but some awareness can be engendered at primary level.

Sampling is a very important statistical activity and there is a great deal of theory written about it. All that is appropriate at Key Stages 1 and 2 is that an effort should be made to make the sample unbiased or 'fair'. The aim is to make the sample representative, but there will be an element of luck in whether it achieves this. A simple way to get a sample of six children from a class of 29 children (14 boys and 15 girls) is to allocate each child a number from 1–29 and draw numbers from a hat. This might produce a biased sample – but that in part depends on the purpose of the sampling. Asking for volunteers or delegating a child to pick five others is not likely to produce a representative sample. If gender is likely to be an important factor, then separately choosing three boys and three girls would be better. If the class had ten boys and 19 girls then two boys and four girls would be more

appropriate. Generally, a simple random sample will be most suitable. This is where:

- each member of the population is equally likely to be selected, and
- members are chosen independently of each other.

Collecting data from the whole population

It is likely that when using the class as subjects, the whole population will be taken which will avoid the need for sampling. When Jason interviews the whole of Class 5A and finds that the most popular sport is netball there is no uncertainty about it, since everyone has been consulted. What does Jason conclude?

'Netball is the favourite sport for Class 5A at Oakfield School.'
Jason. Class 5A. 1st March 1994

The class then discuss whether Jason's results can have any wider bearing:

- Can we conclude anything about the parallel Year 5 class called Class 5B?

- Can we conclude anything about all of Year 5?
- Can we conclude anything about the pupils in Class 5A in one year's time?
- Can we conclude anything about next year's Class 5A?

Now we are trying to go beyond the data and uncertainty must enter again. Jason was registering opinions – and opinions vary from individual to individual and may change with time. We may feel that his results will be a pretty good guide to what a similar survey of Class 5B would say because they are the same age in the same school. We might be justified in treating Jason's complete survey of Class 5A as a sample of Year 5 (that is, Class 5A and 5B combined). With our encouragement, Jason wrote:

'Netball is the favourite sport for Year 5 children at Oakfield School.'
Jason. Class 5A. 1st March 1994.

Sampling always involves making assumptions. In this case Jason assumes that there is no special difference between Class 5A and Class 5B. This seems reasonable. The head tells him that allocation to the two classes is 'at random' – whatever that means! Even so it would be a sensible precaution to check that Class 5A doesn't have a preponderance of girls and Class 5B a preponderance of boys.

The above discussion indicates the very rich nature of data handling work concerning surveys. Children derive great enjoyment from conducting surveys of all kinds – and particularly those of a personal nature (although sensitive issues need careful handling or avoiding). Children like to be interviewed and to express opinions. So do mums and dads (usually) and grandparents and elderly relatives and neighbours (invariably). Links with other curriculum areas can be particularly strong through well-planned surveys.

Pupils will need encouragement from the teacher to go beyond stage **P** (Pose a question), stage **C** (Collect the data), and stage **A** (Analyse the results) and on to stage **I** (Interpret the findings). This should include

47

constructive criticism of the methodology and discussion of what exactly can be concluded (inferred) beyond the bare result.

Statistical understanding

There are two key factors.

The first key factor is awareness of variability:
- not all Class 3 are 1m 5cm tall;
- not all leaves on the tree have the same shape;
- not all tossed coins land heads;
- not all Class 2 get 7m 17cm when measuring the length of the classroom;
- not all Class 1 rank the ice cream flavours vanilla, strawberry, mint, lime, pistachio in the same order.

The second key factor is awareness of chance or randomness:
- If Joanne chooses the six children to interview (see pages 42 – 43) by drawing names out of a hat containing all the names of Class 5A pupils then any six can be selected, including her six friends. On the other hand, she might pick the class's six fanatical Manchester United supporters; probably she will get some boys and some girls; probably they will have a mixture of favourite sports and so on.

– When tossing ten coins together (or one ten times) it is possible to get nine heads and one tail; whatever results is in itself unlikely (i.e. hard to predict) – even the most likely outcome, 5 heads and 5 tails, only occurs on average once every four times.

Both these aspects should be given emphasis throughout the primary years, to gradually engender a sound understanding. This is not easy. A famous statistician has this to say:

'Guided experience with randomness in earlier years is an important prerequisite to successful teaching of formal probability. It is no accident that mathematical probability originated in the study of games of chance, one of the few settings in which simple random phenomena are observed often enough to display clear long-term patterns. Teaching can attempt to recapitulate this historical development... But whether such experience occurs early or late in a student's development it takes significant time to gain appropriate insight into the behaviour of random events.'

David Moore, 'Uncertainty' in *On the Shoulders of Giants – New Approaches to Numeracy* Steen, L.A. (ed.) (National Research Council, USA, 1990)

Computer database programs

Software is available for primary schools which will help with the construction of questionnaires and print them out for use. *Junior Pinpoint* from Longman Logotron goes further – it automatically sets up a database ready to receive the results for analysis. It is a specially-adapted version of *Pinpoint* which is a commercial package. Both versions are available to schools for Archimedes computers. *Pinpoint* is also available for PC computers which have Windows version 3.1 or later.

Figure 18 depicts an idea for a survey taken from the Children's Guide which accompanies *Junior Pinpoint*.

THE CRISP SURVEY

Here is an idea for a survey which you might like to try.

Lots of people like crisps and they all have a favourite flavour, but can they really tell the difference?

Start by conducting a survey amongst your friends using the 'crisps' file on the disc. Remember you can change the form so that it includes your choice of flavours and manufacturers.

Now design some experiments to test whether they can really tell the difference between their favourite crisp and other flavours and makes.

Here is an example form you could use or you could create your own or modify this one.

THE GREAT CRISP SURVEY

How old are you?__ years

How many packets of crisps do you eat per week?

☐ 0 – 3 packets   ☐ 8 – 10 packets
☐ 4 – 7 packets   ☐ More then ten packets

The crisps in bowls A to D are different flavours.
Eat one crisp from each bowl and record the flavour you think it is.

Bowl A	**Bowl B**	**Bowl C**	**Bowl D**
☐ salt and vinegar	☐ salt and vinegar	☐ salt and vinegar	☐ salt and vinegar
☐ cheese and onion	☐ cheese and onion	☐ cheese and onion	☐ cheese and onion
☐ roast chicken	☐ roast chicken	☐ roast chicken	☐ roast chicken
☐ smoky bacon	☐ smoky bacon	☐ smoky bacon	☐ smoky bacon

When you have conducted enough tests examine your data to find out whether people can tell the difference or not. Can you design other experiments? Can you make your own crisps?

Part 3: Crisp Manufacturers

The crisps in bowls E to H are all different makes of plain (ready salted) crisp.
Eat one crisp from each bowl and record which make you think it is.

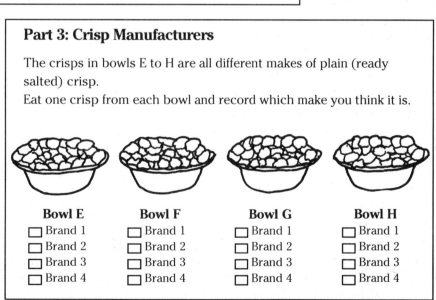

Bowl E	**Bowl F**	**Bowl G**	**Bowl H**
☐ Brand 1	☐ Brand 1	☐ Brand 1	☐ Brand 1
☐ Brand 2	☐ Brand 2	☐ Brand 2	☐ Brand 2
☐ Brand 3	☐ Brand 3	☐ Brand 3	☐ Brand 3
☐ Brand 4	☐ Brand 4	☐ Brand 4	☐ Brand 4

It would be interesting to compare the prices of different crisps. Are more expensive crisps better than cheaper ones? Can you design an experiment to find out? (Use *Junior Pinpoint* to record the results of your experiment).

Figure 18

Junior Pinpoint has the following features:
- **Creating the database** – children create the database when they design a questionnaire (or form) using simple on-screen commands to specify the type of answer expected: numbers, words or dates. Multiple choice questions can also be designed.
- **Collecting the data** – the form can be printed out and copied, then used to collect the data. The information is then read off the form and typed into the computer which displays on screen a copy of the form.
- **Analysing the data** – the data can be displayed a form at a time or condensed into a table – like a spreadsheet – for simple analysis (largest, average...). Graphical display is also possible – pie chart, bar chart, line graph, scatter graph.

Note that *Interpretation and conclusions* are left to the user.

Using apparatus

Collecting data can be the result of conducting experiments rather than going out and interviewing or observing. This is often neglected and can be a valuable aspect of data handling work. Apparatus can be prepared or collected by the teacher or can be bought specially. One commercial kit with a long pedigree is now described. If this particular kit does not appeal, or if the school budget does not stretch this far, the enterprising teacher may construct something along similar lines or find some willing parents to lend a hand.

The original *DIME Probability Kit*, introduced in 1977, has now been updated and in its new form consists of two separate packs (A and B). Each pack has six sets of four sealed tubes containing dice, counters or beads which can be quickly and safely shaken. There is a workcard for each tube (see Figure 19), and a special recording chart.

The *DIME* kit can be used successfully at Key Stage 2, with simple experiments. The *DIME* recording sheet, not described here, is rather difficult for younger children to cope with but is suitable for more able children in upper Key Stage 2. A description of the old kit and the recording chart was published in *Teaching Statistics* in 1982, written by its inventor Geoff Giles. A review of the new kit will be published in a forthcoming issue of *Teaching Statistics*.

The use of sealed tubes containing dice, counters and so on reduces the noise and confusion associated with probability experiments. The innovative teacher who cannot afford the authentic kit can improvise – using transparent plastic tubs covered with cling film or polythene, for example.

Probability is a particularly difficult area and a casual acquaintance with chance events is unlikely to instil the important concepts but rather leave the child with misconceptions (which often carry into adulthood). In order to develop real understanding, children need to take part in suitable experiments. The *DIME* materials were devised specifically to provide a basis for such experiments. This is one area of data handling where rather contrived

DIME Probability   **Pack A**

Card 3

THREE NUMBERED COUNTERS

> The tube contains:
> 3 counters, marked
> 1, 2 or 3 on one side.

First experiment

TRIAL: Shake the tube and put it down on its side

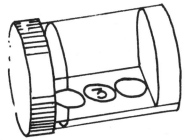

You WIN if:
The 3 is showing.
Otherwise you LOSE.

Second experiment

TRIAL: Shake the tube and put it down on its side.

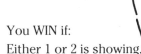

You WIN if:
Either 1 or 2 is showing,
or if both are showing.
Otherwise you LOSE.

Third experiment

TRIAL: Shake the tube and put it down on its side.

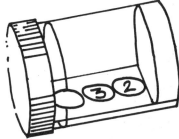

You WIN if:
The sum of the numbers showing is 3 or more.
Otherwise you LOSE.

Figure 19: *DIME Probability Kit* **workcards with illustrations of sealed tubes.**

situations are unavoidable – at least they can be put into game form, and collecting data can be fun!

Sources of secondary data

The bulk of this chapter has been about collecting data from primary sources (that is, being directly involved in their collection oneself). It makes sense, however, to check whether the data already exist in an accessible form. When tapping into such a source, one is collecting *secondary* data. This is important. Every school library needs to

have sources of data which children can turn to. The Resources chapter at the end of this book contains many suggestions for sources for data. A brief selective summary is included here to emphasise that this is not meant to be a marginal optional activity, but an integral part of handling data in the primary school.

Sources and ideas:

– Newspapers – both local and national – building a cuttings library.
– The ten-yearly national *Census of Population* reports available at local libraries (the last one took place in 1991).
– *Social Trends*, an annual government publication prepared by the Central

Statistical Office (CSO) and published by HMSO. This covers such categories as: Population, Households and Families, Leisure, Transport.

- Publications of OXFAM, Save The Children, and so on and books such as the *Third World Directory*. These are good for Third World comparisons on topics of interest to children.
- Publications about animals: WWF (World Wide Fund for Nature), RSPB (Royal Society for the Protection of Birds) and so on.
- Road Safety, Fire Prevention, and similar booklets.
- Local bodies (local authorities often have Yearbooks, leisure centres may have brochures and reports).
- Regional bodies (such as police forces).
- National bodies and groups (such as Forestry Commission, Consumers' Association).
- International bodies (such as World Bank, UNESCO).
- Fact books (such as Penguin's *Facts in Focus, Guinness Book of Records*).
- Databases which accompany database programs.
- Parish records – births, marriages, deaths.
- Electoral rolls.
- District health records.
- Court records.
- Probate records.
- School log books.

Refer to Chapter 10 for more information about resources.

Chapter Three
Analysing data – graphs and diagrams in the National Curriculum

We now turn to the third stage of the **PCAI** cycle, analysing data. The particular data handling tool we will focus on is a range of useful graphs and diagrams. Chapters 3 and 4 are devoted to looking at the sorts of graphs and diagrams that children can use, both to explore patterns in their data and to re-present information more clearly for others.

The distinction between *graphs* and *diagrams* is not always clearly made and indeed these two terms are sometimes used to describe the same thing. However, within the area of data handling, there is a fairly clear

distinction. *Diagrams* tend to be less precise forms of representation, where relationships and connections are indicated in a fairly loose way. *Graphs*, on the other hand, are more precise: the position of a point or the length of a line is a measure of something. The position of the top of a bar or a point on a graph corresponds to some particular numerical value.

In Chapter 4, the technical properties of common graphs and diagrams are described. Here, in Chapter 3, we examine how data handling ideas are presented in Attainment

Sorting and counting

Target 5 of the National Curriculum document. Listed throughout the chapter are all the relevant programmes of study and statements of attainment (excluding those concerned with probability) up to Level 6. Much of this is fairly straightforward and not discussed further, but the terminology that has been italicised in these extracts is explained and clarified in the sections which follow. Also, where possible, we have tried to indicate the overall development of the ideas as pupils move through the Levels from 1 to 6. In general terms, the three central ideas contained here are:
• sorting and counting (Attainment Target 5 Levels 1 and 2);
• measuring (Attainment Target 5 Levels 3 to 5) and
• relationships (Attainment Target 5 Level 6).
    These three themes have been used to form the central headings for the chapter.

Sorting things into sets is an important idea in mathematics, particularly at Key Stages 1 and 2. To be successful at sorting, children need to be clear about exactly what distinguishes the objects being sorted ('choosing criteria to sort') and to be able to name the sets according to their criteria so that they can 'classify' them.
    Mapping diagrams (sometimes called Arrow diagrams) are simply ways of showing on paper which item belongs to which category. For example, a mapping diagram showing what type of cooker, gas or electric,

the children have at home can be seen in Figure 1.

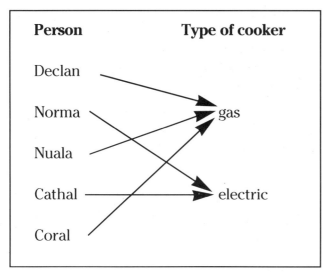

Figure 1

A further example of a mapping diagram is given in Chapter 4, page 62.

A natural follow-up to any sorting activity is to count the number of items in each set. This might involve doing some kind of tally (actually the first mention of *tallying* does not occur until Level 3, but the procedure is quite straightforward and is a good preparation for work at Level 3) and the results can then be shown in a frequency table. Here is an example in which the children were asked to decide where they wished to go on a school trip. Each child's suggestion was collected, as shown in Figure 2.

Person	Suggestion
Declan	Seaside
Norma	Theme Park
Nuala	Cinema
Cathal	Theme Park
Coral	Alton Towers

Figure 2

The next stage was to tally the different suggestions. First, however, they needed to clarify the various categories, for example the suggestions 'Theme Park' and 'Alton Towers'

were essentially the same thing and so became a single category. Two of the many different ways of tallying are shown in Figure 3.

Suggestion	Tally
Theme Park	XXXXX XXXXX XX
Seaside	XXXX
Cinema	XXXXX XXX
Museum	XX
Circus	XXX

Suggestion	Tally
Theme Park	卌 卌 II
Seaside	IIII
Cinema	卌 III
Museum	II
Circus	III

Figure 3

It is quite a good idea to group the tally marks in fives, as has been done here, to make the counting easier. From the tally chart, the *frequency table* can be constructed (Figure 4).

Suggestion	Frequency
Theme Park	12
Seaside	4
Cinema	8
Museum	2
Circus	3
TOTAL	29

Figure 4

Including the 'Total' figure at the bottom provides a check that no one has been missed out or double-counted.

Three useful diagrams for showing how things have been sorted or classified are *Carroll diagrams*, *Venn diagrams* and *tree diagrams*, and these are explained in Chapter 5.

Measuring

Level 3

Programme of study

'• constructing and interpreting bar charts and graphs (pictograms) where the symbol represents a group of units.'

Statement of attainment

'Construct and interpret statistical diagrams.'

Level 4

Programmes of study

'• specifying an issue for which data are needed.'
'• collecting, grouping and ordering discrete data using tallying methods and creating a frequency table for grouped data.'
'• constructing and interpreting bar-line and line graphs and frequency diagrams with suitable class intervals for *discrete variables*.'
'• creating a decision tree diagram with questions to sort and identify a collection of objects.'
'• understanding, calculating and using the mean and range of a set of data.'

Statements of attainment

'• Conduct a survey on an issue of their choice.'
'• Use the mean and range of a set of data.'

Level 5

Programmes of study

'• designing and using an observation sheet to collect data; collating and analysing results.'
'• collecting, ordering and grouping continuous data using equal class intervals and creating frequency tables.'
'• constructing and interpreting pie charts from a collection of data with a few variables.'
'• constructing and interpreting conversion graphs.'
'• constructing and interpreting frequency diagrams and choosing class intervals for a continuous variable.'

Statements of attainment

'• Design and use an observation sheet to collect data.'
'• Interpret statistical diagrams.'

Sorting and counting involve putting collections of similar objects together and asking questions of the form 'how many?' A rather more sophisticated way of describing things is to carry out some form of measurement directly on individual objects, perhaps weighing or timing each one. Direct measurement of this nature gives rise to questions of the form 'how much?' Although measure is included in AT2, measurement is often the means by which pupils will collect their data (stage **C** of the **PCAI** cycle) and so is a crucial means of generating data in AT5.

The Level 4 Programme of Study requiring pupils to be engaged in 'specifying an issue for which data are needed' can be related to stage **P** of the **PCAI** cycle. This appears to be the first occasion in AT5 where pupils are required, explicitly, to focus on the purpose and relevance of data handling. However, this delay is clearly not what was intended and it makes good sense for pupils of all ages to be regularly placed in situations where their data handling really means something.

The term 'variable' is normally used to describe something which can be measured or counted or observed and which is capable of taking various (at least two) different values. Here are some examples of variables:

• **coins** – the number of coins in different people's purses;
• **sex** – the sex of each baby born during a week in a hospital;
• **age** – the ages of children in a school;

• **score** – the scores from tossing a die repeatedly;
• **weight** – the weights (or 'masses') of various parcels.

The actual value of each of these measures will depend on whose purse, which person or what parcel is being considered. If different purses, people and parcels are measured, a variety of different data values are produced. 'Number of coins in a purse' will always come out to be an exact whole number. This is an example of a 'discrete' variable (Level 4) so called because things like coins are counted in discrete steps: 0, 1, 2, 3 and so on.

There are actually two types of discrete variable – *numbers* and *categories*. 'Number of coins in a purse' is clearly of the former type, whereas a variable such as a person's mode of transport to school will usually be classified into one of several possible categories (car, bus, on foot).

Variables like age or weight can never be measured with perfect accuracy since they do not occur in a discrete set of possible values. Age and weight are known as 'continuous' variables (Level 5) because they can be measured on a continuous scale of measurement. In theory, there is no limit to the degree of accuracy to which a continuous

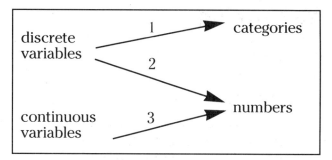

Figure 5: Three types of variable.

variable can be measured and, therefore, there is no limit to the number of possible values that such a variable can take. For example, we could say a child was seven years old, or seven years six months, or seven years six months four days and so on.

There are, then, three types of variable that are worth distinguishing, two of which are numerical and one categorical. Their connection is summarised in Figure 5.

It is useful to be able to distinguish different types of data, chiefly because the nature of the data is a key factor in helping you decide how best to graph and analyse the data.

Figure 6 gives some more examples of each of these three types of variable and also an indication of what sort of graph is suitable for which data type.

Type	Data	Graphs	Example
DISCRETE DATA	categories	tally chart pictogram pie chart Carroll diagram Venn diagram tree diagram	favourite colours means of transport to school ability to tie a bow (or not)
	numbers	bar chart	number of coins in people's purses scores from tossing a die number of milk bottles each family takes daily
CONTINUOUS DATA	numbers	number line histogram stemplot	height weight age time temperature

Figure 6

Relationships

All the previous examples have involved data which have been collected for one single variable at a time. This can be extended. For example, pupils may wish to collect a variety of information about each person in their class. This could include measuring variables such as the ages or the running times of each child. They could then decide to look at age or running time as separate variables.

An alternative, and more sophisticated approach, is to look at age and running time together and to use these pairs of values to explore the *relationship* between the age and running time of the children in the class. The easiest way to do this is to plot the paired values on to a scatter graph and look for some pattern in how the points seem to lie on the graph (Figure 7).

There are two central ideas to be interpreted from the scatter graph, which can be summarised by the following two questions:
• What (if any) basic relationship is there between the two variables and hence can we predict one from the other?

• How strong is the relationship? (what is the strength of correlation between the variables?)

These two questions – the nature of the relationship and the strength of the relationship – are now explored in some detail.

What is the basic relationship?

The first question to be explored in this example concerns the nature of the relationship between age and running time – do older children tend to take longer to run a race (showing a positive relationship between age and running time) or is the pattern of points in the other direction (showing a negative relationship between age and running time)? The conclusion to this question will be based on whether the points appear to fall generally in a pattern from bottom left to top right on the graph, or from top left to bottom right.

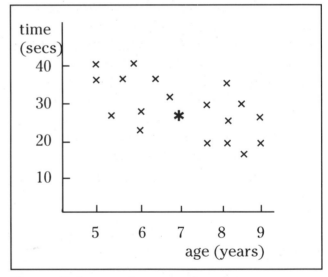

Figure 7: Age against running time.

The overall trend shown in Figure 7 is negative (the pattern of points slopes from top left to bottom right), suggesting that the greater the age of the child, the less time they are likely to take to run the race. An additional point, marked with a '✳', has been added here. It represents the average age (measured on the horizontal scale) and the average time (measured on the vertical scale) and is found by calculating, separately, the mean of each variable.

Another example of a possible relationship between two variables is the one between the height and the weight of each of a sample of children. (It should be noted that children are often rather self-conscious about their weight or height. Clearly such an investigation should be handled sensitively or some alternative investigation found. For example, they could plot time taken to get to school against distance each pupil lives away from school.) Alternatively, they could plot the time each child takes to count to 50 against the time to recite or read aloud the alphabet. Another pair of measures to explore could be the time taken to hop across the room against the time taken to walk backwards. Body measures are also good contexts for exploring relationships, for example handspan against foot length, head circumference against height and so on.

It is often a good idea to draw a line which best seems to illustrate the underlying pattern of points, as has been done here. This is sometimes known as the 'best-fit line' because it is the line which best fits the points on the scatter graph. One property of the best-fit line is that it should pass through the centre point (marked with a '✱' in the previous example).

If the best-fit line goes from bottom left to top right, it is said to have a positive slope. This is the case in Figures 8 and 9 and this situation is one where the underlying

relationship is positive (that is both measurements seem to increase together). When the best-fit line slopes in the opposite direction (as in Figure 10), from top left to bottom right, this suggests a negative relationship. Another example of this is the relationship between the price of, say, tomatoes and the quantity bought by people. As the price of tomatoes decreases over the season, most people will buy more. So, in general, there is a negative relationship between the price of tomatoes and the amount people will buy of them.

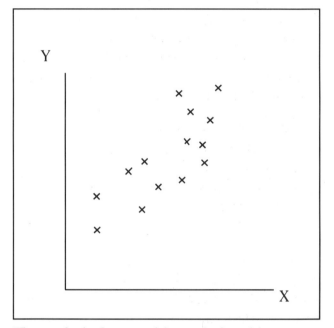

Figure 9: A clear positive relationship

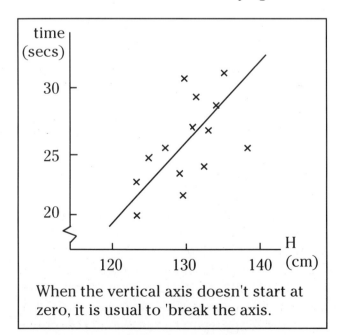

When the vertical axis doesn't start at zero, it is usual to 'break the axis.

Figure 8: Age against running time.

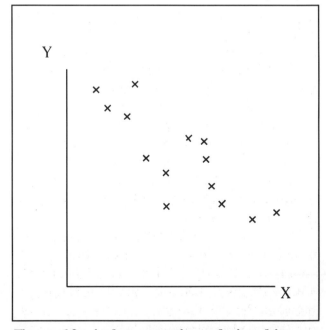

Figure 10: A clear negative relationship.

How strong is the relationship?

The second important pattern to explore is how widely scattered the points are. This gives an indication of the strength of the relationship in question, otherwise known as the *correlation*, for example between height and weight. Again, with the best-fit line drawn in, it may be easier to make an assessment by eye of how strong the correlation is. In the example shown in Figure 8, the points lie quite close to the best-fit line so the correlation is fairly strong. Figure 11 shows a scatter of points with no clear relationship so the correlation is extremely weak.

In more advanced statistical work, there are formal methods for calculating the best-fit line and for finding a numerical measure of the strength of the correlation, but at primary level it is enough just to begin to think and talk about these ideas and start to develop some intuitions about them in simple situations. These discussions can begin even with young children as they are experiencing and describing relationships from a very early age. Here are three examples of remarks made by the same child, Carrie, over a three-year period:

'The more the long time, the littler my balloon grows.'
Carrie (aged 4 years)
'Eddie says that the longer your legs, the faster you can run.'
Carrie (aged 5 years)
'Ah, I see. So the higher the number on the pencil, the harder the lead.'
Carrie (aged 6 years)

From *Investigating Statistics – A Beginner's Guide* Alan Graham (Hodder & Stoughton, 1990).

The next chapter is a summary and explanation of the graphs mentioned below:
– mapping (or arrow) diagram
– tally chart
– frequency table
– pictogram
– bar chart
– pie chart
– tree diagram
– Venn diagram
– Carroll diagram
– number line
– histogram
– stemplot (also known as a Stem-and-leaf diagram)
– scatter graph.

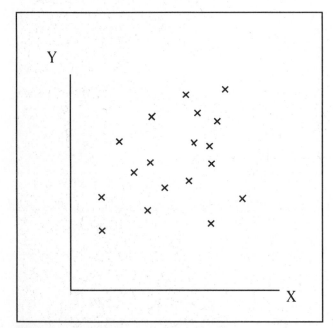

Figure 11: No clear relationship.

Chapter Four
Analysing data – Esther's eggsellent graphs

This chapter outlines and explains the main graphs and diagrams which pupils at Key Stages 1 and 2 would be expected to know about. For further reading in this area, see the references given at the end of the chapter.

Esther keeps seven hens in her garden and makes careful records of their feeding and laying habits. Her data are summarised in a variety of graphical representations, along with a brief description of each diagram or graph and when its use is appropriate.

1 Mapping (or Arrow) diagram

Esther has noticed that only three of her hens, Blackie, Bessie and Rhodie are good layers, while the other four are not. One way of representing this information is to use a mapping diagram, as follows:

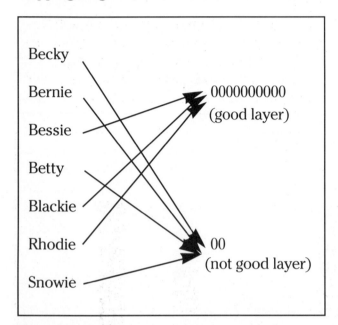

Figure 1: Mapping diagram showing the good layers.

2 Tally chart/Frequency table

In Figure 2 the tally chart and frequency table have been combined into a single table, but of course each can be drawn separately.

3 Pictogram

There are various ways of drawing a tally chart but grouping in fives, as has been done in Figure 2, is the most commonly-used. It is quite easy, even for very young children, to re-present this sort of information in the form of a pictogram, using rows of pictures, where each picture represents one (or five or ten) of the objects in question.

In the pictogram in Figure 3, each **0** represents one egg.

Blackie **0000000000000000000000000000000**

Betty **000000000000000000**

Becky **0000000000000000**

Bessie **000000000000000000000000**

Bernie **000000**

Snowie **0000000000000000**

Rhodie **0000000000000000000000000**

Figure 3: A pictogram showing the number of eggs laid by each of Esther's hens in one month.

Name of Hen	Tally	Frequency
Blackie	卌 卌 卌 卌 卌 IIII	29
Betty	卌 卌 卌 II	17
Becky	卌 卌 卌	15
Bessie	卌 卌 卌 卌 IIII	24
Bernie	卌 I	6
Snowie	卌 卌 卌 I	16
Rhodie	卌 卌 卌 卌 IIII	24

Figure 2: Number of eggs each hen laid in one month.

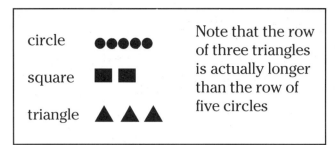

circle	●●●●●	Note that the row of three triangles is actually longer than the row of five circles
square	■ ■	
triangle	▲ ▲ ▲	

Figure 4: A misleading pictogram.

Note that another name for a pictogram is a *pictograph* or, less commonly, an *ideograph*.

It is important to check that the icons of a pictogram all take up the same space on the page, otherwise a misleading impression is created. For example, ten children were asked to record their favourite mathematical shape. Five chose a circle, three a square and two a triangle. Figure 4 illustrates how misleading it can be if these icons are not drawn to the same scale.

4 Bar chart

Block graph is a general term for a graph consisting of columns or bars. A *bar chart* is a particular form of block graph in which the bars are drawn with gaps between them. For example, Figures 5 and 6 show two ways of

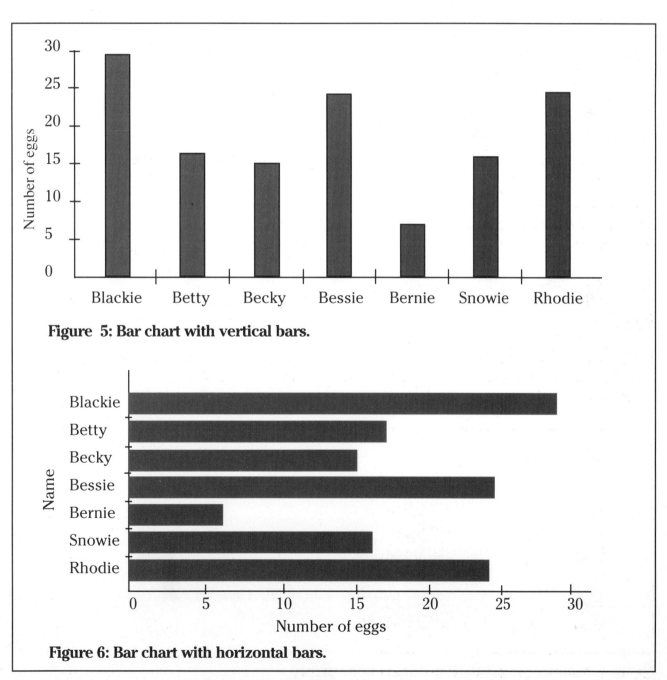

Figure 5: Bar chart with vertical bars.

Figure 6: Bar chart with horizontal bars.

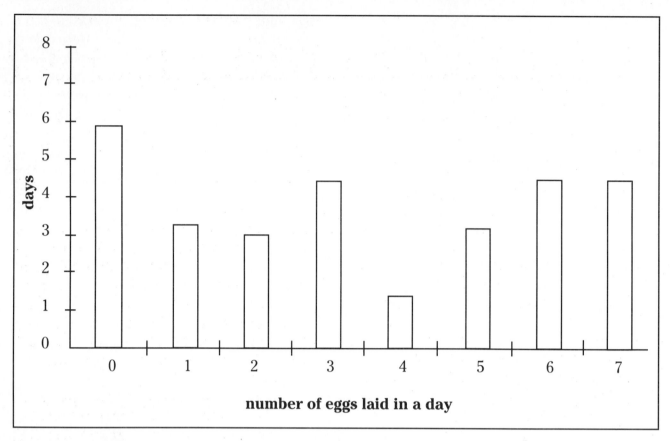

Figure 7: Number of eggs laid by 7 hens in one month

representing the number of eggs laid by each of Esther's hens in one month, the first chart with vertical bars and the second with horizontal bars.

Note that in this example the order in which the bars have been placed is quite arbitrary, although this is not necessarily always the case.

Although bar charts usually show categorical data (that is data representing a count of the numbers of items in different categories), it can also depict numerical data provided these are discrete, as the example in Figure 7 shows. Here the horizontal scale shows the number of eggs laid each day. Because such numbers do have a natural sequence, the corresponding bars have to be drawn in this particular order.

In this example, the bars have been drawn particularly narrowly, to emphasise that, although these are numbers, they are discrete. Indeed, the bars can even be thin lines. This type of bar chart is sometimes called a *stick graph* because the bars look like sticks.

Some things to remember about bar charts:
• The bars should all have the same width, otherwise a misleading impression can be given about the relative importance of each bar.
• There should be clear gaps between adjacent bars, otherwise the false impression could be given that there is some sort of continuous number scale on the horizontal axis. They should also be equally spaced.
• There are two basic types of data, discrete and continuous, and the distinction between them was discussed earlier (see page 57). Bar charts should only be used to display discrete data. The two examples given earlier illustrate two different sorts of discrete data – in Figure 5 the horizontal axis shows discrete *categories*, while in Figure 7 the horizontal axis shows discrete *numbers*.
• It is worth thinking about the order in which the bars are shown and whether a more interesting or useful order could be used instead.
• The bar labels are centred under each bar on the horizontal axis, unlike histograms

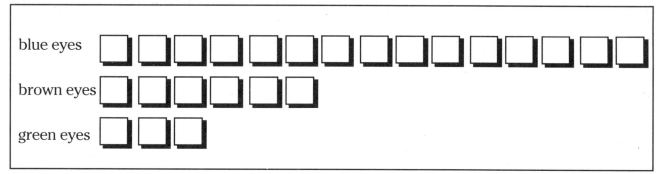

Figure 8: A Unifix bar chart showing eye colour.

where the horizontal scale is marked at the points where the adjacent columns of the histogram touch. Histograms are described in more detail in section 9, page 69.

Young children can construct and handle their own 3-D bar charts using Unifix cubes, cotton reels or Multilink (Figure 8 illustrates the eye colours in a class).

Note that the cubes can either be placed horizontally in a line on the desk, as shown in Figure 8, or stacked vertically. Offering the pupils cubes of unequal size can be a useful means of provoking further comment and discussion!

5 Pie chart

Some things to remember about pie charts:
• Like bar charts, pie charts should only be used to display discrete data. However, it is usual to restrict the use of a pie chart to depict discrete *categories*, and not discrete

numbers as shown in Figure 7. The reason for this is that it makes more sense to place numbers on a horizontal line rather than in a circular arrangement where the order of the numbers tends to be lost.
• It is worth thinking about the order in which the sectors of the pie are shown, and whether a more interesting or useful order could be used instead.
• There is an important feature of a pie chart, which distinguishes it from the bar chart. It is that a pie chart should be used to describe a situation which actually represents something that is a complete whole. Where this does not apply, a pie chart should not be used. For example, a pie chart showing the prices charged in various shops for the same bar of chocolate would be rather meaningless (Figure 10), since the complete pie would correspond to the sum of all the different prices. Taken together, these prices don't add up to anything very useful or interesting.

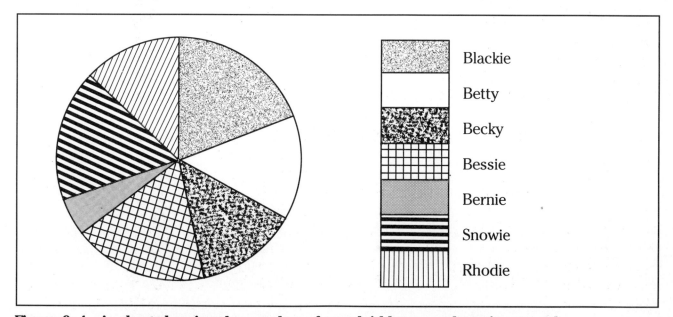

Figure 9: A pie chart showing the number of eggs laid by seven hens in a month.

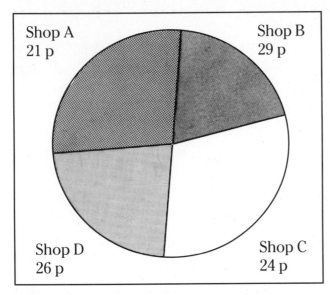

Figure 10: A meaningless pie chart showing chocolate bar prices.

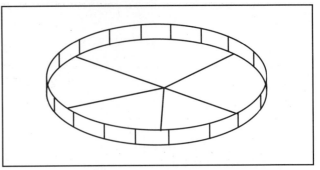

Figure 11: Strip graph forming a pie chart.

A useful introduction to both the bar chart and pie chart is to use a *strip graph*. For the example of the 131 eggs laid in one month, the children can start by cutting from squared paper a narrow strip of paper which is, say, 131mm long. They can then colour in the sections corresponding to each hen (Figure 11).

A bar chart can then be made by cutting up the strip into separate lengths and sticking them on to pre-drawn axes. To make a pie chart, the strip can be twisted into a circle and glued to a page. The centre of the circle can be estimated and the sectors drawn in from the marks on the strip (note that there are no awkward calculations involved here). When dealing with data about themselves (favourite pop star, month of birth and so on), the children can create human bar charts by standing in the appropriate columns. By holding hands in their column and then joining on to the others, they can open up to form a circle – a human pie chart! The effect can be completed by tying pieces of coloured ribbon to a central point and stretching the pieces out to the 'boundary' children.

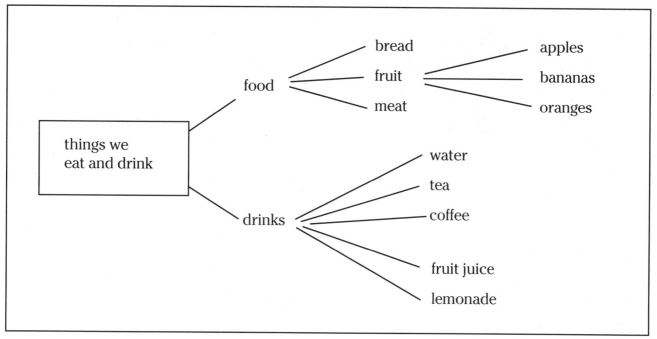

Figure 12: Tree diagram showing things we eat and drink.

6 Tree diagram

Tree diagrams are useful for representing how ideas are organised in terms of their structure and hierarchies. As the name implies, the diagram can be thought of as a tree with a central idea (the trunk) sub-divided into its various branches and twigs, as shown in Figure 12.

Figure 13 is another simple tree diagram to illustrate that a bar chart and a histogram are both types of block graph.

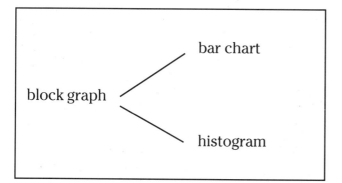

Figure 13: Tree diagram of block graphs.

7 Venn diagram

Another way of representing how things are sorted and classified is to use a Venn diagram. For example, Esther kept a note of where her hens tended to lay their eggs and found that four of them laid inside the henhouse, two went outside, and one of the hens did both. This could be represented as follows:

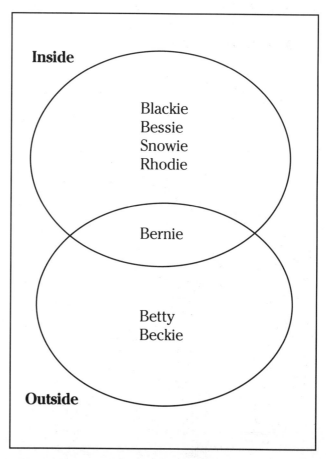

Figure 14: Venn diagram showing where the hens lay their eggs.

8 Carroll diagram

Continuing with the theme of sorting, a Carroll diagram in its most common form is a two-by-two table used to sort things according to two different criteria at the same time. For example, we could look at both whether or not the hens were black, and whether or not they were good layers. All five of Esther's hens whose names begin with the letter 'B' are black and the other two are not black. Only three of the hens are good layers (anything over 20 eggs per month is 'good'). If Esther wanted to find out whether there was a link between a hen's colour and how good a layer it was, she might find the Carroll diagram in Figure 15 useful:

	good layer	not good layer
black hen	Blackie Bessie	Betty Becky Bernie
not black hen	Rhodie	Snowie

Figure 15

Note how the row and column headings have been written in the general form of 'A'/'Not A' and 'B'/'not B'. This emphasises an important property of a Carroll diagram, namely that all possible outcomes have been included, whether reading horizontally or vertically.

This diagram can now be redrawn showing the *number* of hens in each cell (Figure 16).

	good layer	not good layer
black hen	2	3
not black hen	1	1

Figure 16

Carroll diagrams are often drawn with the row and column totals added (Figure 17).

	good layer	not good layer	total
black hen	2	3	5
not black hen	1	1	2
total	3	4	7

Figure 17

For young children, the Carroll diagram can be drawn on the floor in chalk and they can place, into the appropriate cell, cards showing the picture or name of each item. Where it is being used to represent data about themselves, the Carroll diagram could even be drawn large enough for the children to stand in the cells themselves. For example, the teacher could make a large Carroll diagram on the floor using rubber mats and mark the cells using card, as in Figure 18.

	black hair	not black hair
blue eyes		
not blue eyes		

Figure 18

The game is for the children to jump into the right box as quickly as possible.

9 Number line and histogram

Esther noticed that the eggs of young hens were much smaller and lighter in weight than the eggs of more mature birds. She weighed, accurate to the nearest gram, the eggs of two hens of different ages and produced the results shown in Figure 19.

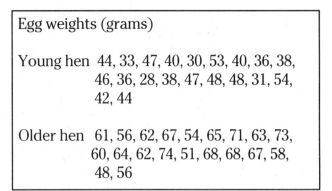

Egg weights (grams)

Young hen 44, 33, 47, 40, 30, 53, 40, 36, 38, 46, 36, 28, 38, 47, 48, 48, 31, 54, 42, 44

Older hen 61, 56, 62, 67, 54, 65, 71, 63, 73, 60, 64, 62, 74, 51, 68, 68, 67, 58, 48, 56

Figure 19

A simple way of representing numbers like these is to use a number line (Figure 20). Each point can be represented with either a 'x' or a '.'

The number line is quite a useful way of seeing at a glance how widely spread the numbers are. However, a better way of seeing the overall 'shape' of the way the numbers are spread is to draw a histogram.

In Figure 13 (page 67), the relationship between a bar chart, histogram and block graph was spelled out as follows:

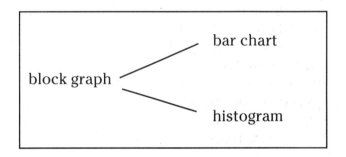

Bearing in mind that bar charts and histograms are two distinct types of block graph, they can be distinguished visually. Bar charts are block graphs that have been drawn

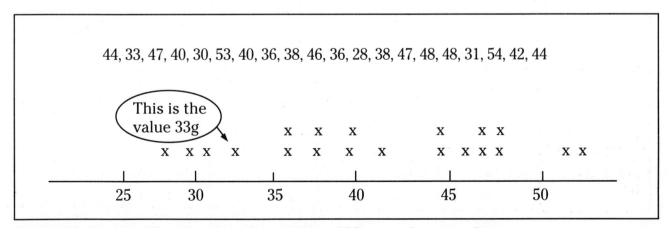

Figure 20: Number line showing the weights of 20 eggs of a young hen.

	Number of eggs laid by	
Weight W in grams	Young hen (frequency)	Older hen (frequency)
$20 \leq W < 30$	1	
$30 \leq W < 40$	7	
$40 \leq W < 50$	10	1
$50 \leq W < 60$	2	5
$60 \leq W < 70$		11
$70 \leq W < 80$		3
TOTAL	20	20

Figure 21: Frequency table showing the two batches of egg weights.

with gaps between the bars. Histograms, on the other hand, are drawn so that the adjacent bars touch each other. This feature reflects the fact that, unlike bar charts, histograms are used to portray continuous data (see the discussion on continuous data in the section on Level 5 Programmes of Study in Chapter 3). Data are usually organised into a frequency table first before being drawn graphically, and this two-staged approach is one that is used here.

The two batches of weights of eggs from each hen can be grouped in 10g bands in the form of a frequency table, as shown in Figure 21.

Notice the way in which the intervals shown in the left-hand column have been written. This has been done to ensure that consecutive intervals will touch but not overlap with each other (Figure 22).

Notice that it would be incorrect to write the intervals as follows:

$$20 \leq W \leq 30$$
$$30 \leq W \leq 40$$
and so on.

This would be unsatisfactory because a weight measured as exactly 30g would belong in both intervals.

The histograms for the two batches of data can now be drawn and compared. In this example (Figures 23 and 24) the intervals are all equally wide, with a width of 10g. Although it is possible to draw histograms with unequal intervals, this creates problems concerning what the height of each column refers to. So it is advisable to stick to histograms with equal-width columns.

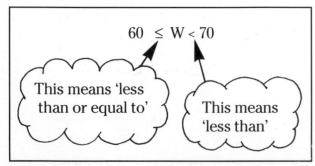

Figure 22

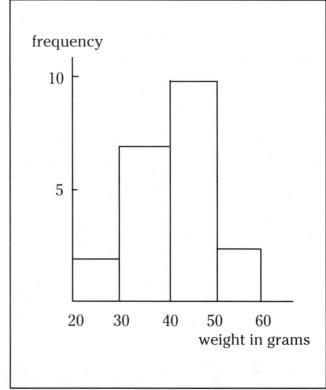

Figure 23: Histogram showing the weights of 20 eggs laid by a young hen.

70

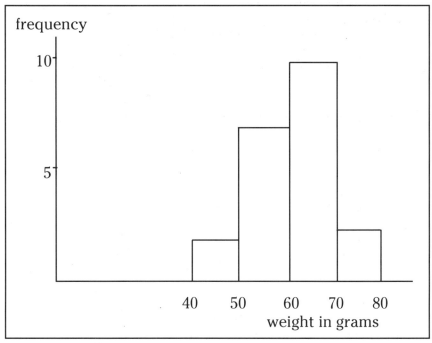

Figure 24: Histogram showing the weights of 20 eggs laid by an older hen

10 Stemplot (Stem-and-leaf diagram)

Figure 25 shows the same data on egg weights represented using a stemplot.

Drawing a stemplot is a two-staged process, and the unsorted version in Figure 25 represents the first stage. Here the 'leaves' have simply been inserted in the order in which each item of data appeared. When a stemplot is used in this way as a means of recording data, there is no alternative but to insert the leaves in this way. However, it is more useful to show the leaves on each stem ranked in order of size. This is the second stage in drawing a stemplot, and the sorted version is shown in Figure 26.

Like the histogram, the stemplot shows the overall 'shape' of a set of numbers. However, its special feature is that all the original data values are retained – you see the values appearing as individual 'leaves' on the display. This allows you to identify from the completed stemplot particular values that are of interest – the largest or the smallest value, the mode, the median value and so on.

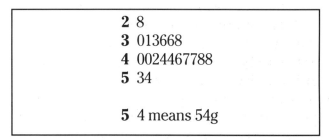

Figure 26: Sorted stemplot showing the weights of 20 eggs.

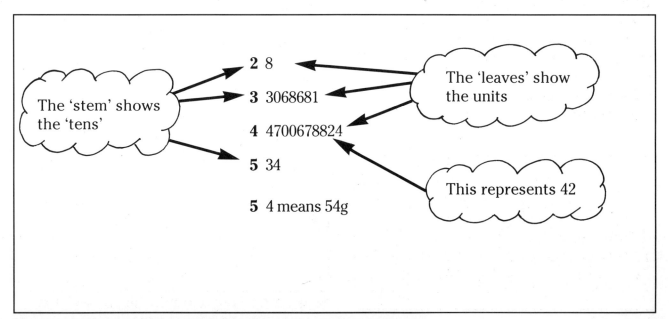

Figure 25: Unsorted stemplot showing the weights of 20 eggs.

Two stemplots can be drawn back-to-back, as shown in Figure 27.

older hen		younger hen
	2	8
	3	0136688
8	**4**	0024467788
86641	**5**	34
88775432210	**6**	
431	**7**	
	5	4 means 54g

Figure 27

11 Scatter graph

The back-to-back stemplot in Figure 27 seems to suggest a relationship between the age of the hen and the weight of the eggs produced. Esther decided to explore this relationship systematically, by collecting paired data (in this case from a sample of eight hens – listed below) about these two factors and drawing the results as a scatter graph (Figure 28).

Age of hen (months)	Average egg weight (g)
4	34
8	53
6	50
5	44
5	49
10	62
7	56
9	54

This scatter graph suggests that there is a positive, but not perfect, relationship between the age of the hen and the weight of egg that she is likely to lay. (Clearly the egg weight will vary from hen to hen anyway.) The relationship is positive because the pattern of points slopes upwards and to the right, suggesting that 'the older the hen, the heavier the egg'. The suggestion that the relationship is not perfect derives from the fact that the points do not lie in a perfect straight line or curve.

One point worth considering when drawing a scatter graph is which factor to put on which axis. In general, the convention is based on the nature of the *dependency* you think there is between the two things. For example, if the children are investigating the relationship between the growth of a plant and the amount of water it is given, ask yourself the question 'is the amount of growth dependent on the amount of water or the

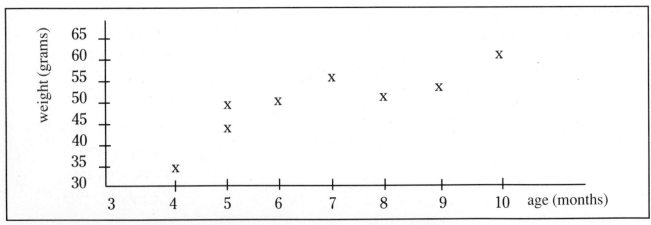

Figure 28: Scatter graph showing age of hen with weight of egg.

other way round?' In this instance it is clear that the *growth* is dependent on the *water*, not the other way round, so we put amount of water on the horizontal axis and plant growth on the vertical axis.

Where it is possible to decide about the likely dependency between the two things under consideration, it is usual to put the independent factor on the horizontal axis and the dependent factor on the vertical axis. The age of a hen cannot be thought to be determined by the weight of egg it lays, whereas a case could be made for thinking that the dependency applied the other way round. For this reason, age, the independent factor, is put on the horizontal axis.

As a rule, measures of time are always independent of everything else and so should be drawn on the horizontal axis.

To end this chapter, a summary of all the graphs and diagrams and how they are connected is given below.

Which graph?

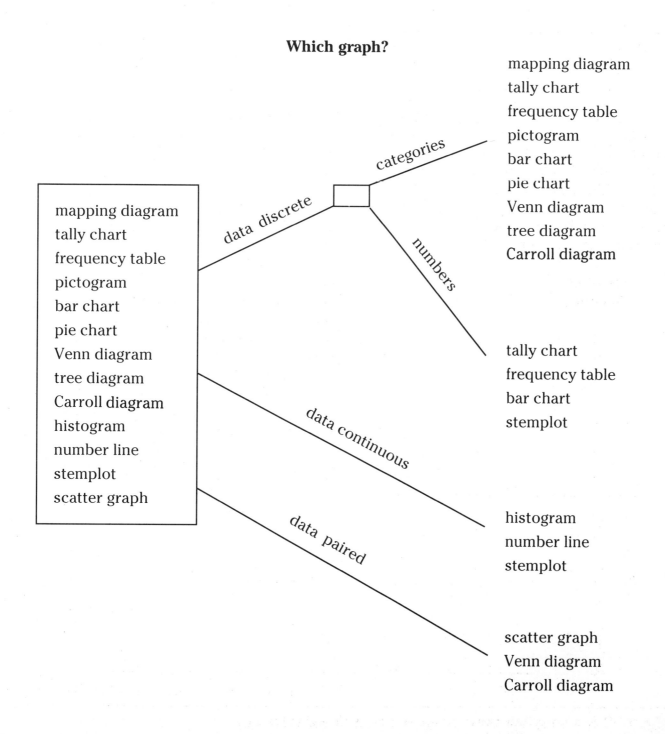

mapping diagram
tally chart
frequency table
pictogram
bar chart
pie chart
Venn diagram
tree diagram
Carroll diagram
histogram
number line
stemplot
scatter graph

data discrete

categories

mapping diagram
tally chart
frequency table
pictogram
bar chart
pie chart
Venn diagram
tree diagram
Carroll diagram

numbers

tally chart
frequency table
bar chart
stemplot

data continuous

histogram
number line
stemplot

data paired

scatter graph
Venn diagram
Carroll diagram

Further reading

Here is a list of publications which you might find useful for developing graph work in the classroom:

Rangecroft, Margaret (1991) 'Graphwork – Developing a Progression Part 1 – The early stages', *Teaching Statistics*, Volume 13, No. 2, pages 44–6.

Rangecroft, Margaret (1991) 'Graphwork – Developing a Progression Part 2 – A diversity of graphs', *Teaching Statistics*, Volume 13, No. 3, pages 90–2.

Graham, Alan (1990) PM649, *Supporting Primary Mathematics, Handling Data*, Centre for Mathematics Education, The Open University.

Chapter Five
Analysing data – using a spreadsheet

This chapter, and the one which follows, continues the theme of 'analysing data' (stage **A** of the **PCAI** cycle). Increasingly, both in and out of school, data analysis is carried out on a computer or calculator. Chapters five and six deal with the use of a spreadsheet and a database respectively. They have been written assuming no previous technical knowledge or teaching experience of either.

It is not realistic to provide a basic introduction to using spreadsheets without being very explicit about the way in which instructions are keyed into the computer. Unfortunately, each commercial spreadsheet package works slightly differently. Because of this, we have had to concentrate on one or two specific packages. Choosing which

packages to focus on was not easy. There is a variety of spreadsheets on the market and they are becoming more powerful and user-friendly all the time. At the time of writing, *Grasshopper* is the most common spreadsheet in use in primary classrooms. *Advantage* and *Eureka!* are two of a newer generation of spreadsheets with many more features and are intuitively easier to use. Although at one level all spreadsheets work on the same basic principle, they do vary in the way that they operate. Even *Grasshopper* will operate in a slightly different way depending on which machine it is running on. This could be an RM Nimbus or one of the Acorn machines – a BBC B, a BBC Master or one of the Acorn Archimedes range.

The two packages, *Grasshopper* and *Eureka!*, have been used as the basis for the detailed descriptions contained in this chapter. For a list of the various spreadsheets currently available, write to NCET (see references at end of chapter).

This chapter contains the following sections:
- What is a spreadsheet? (a basic introduction)
- Using a spreadsheet in the classroom
- Getting started
- Using a spreadsheet in topic work (containing a case study of spreadsheet use in the classroom)
- Using a spreadsheet in the staffroom (a case study of a teacher's professional use of a spreadsheet)

What is a spreadsheet?

Q1: *What does a spreadsheet look like?*
A spreadsheet is a sort of 2-D grid made up of rows and columns. Each little box in the grid is called a 'cell' (Figure 1).

There is more to a spreadsheet than a simple display of information in a grid. There is a variety of powerful commands which allow you to summarise the information or to look for patterns and relationships contained in it. For example, you can find the total or the average of the values in any row or column or copy formulas between cells and, if you wish, display the data using a variety of graphs.

Q2: *What is a spreadsheet used for?*
A spreadsheet is particularly useful for storing and processing data when repeated calculations of the same kind are required. For example, it can be used to investigate questions such as:
- Which size of packet is the best value for money?
- What is the average speed for each of these journeys?
- How much will this journey cost for different groups of people?
- How many calories are contained in different combinations of foods?

Q3: *How can you find your way around a spreadsheet?*
Each cell in the spreadsheet is labelled according to its column and row position. For example, cell B3 is in column B, row 3. You move between adjacent cells using the arrow keys ($\uparrow$, $\rightarrow$, etc.). On certain spreadsheets, special key presses can be used to take you from whichever cell the cursor is currently in to other locations such as the first cell (A1), the last cell and so on.

Q4: *How big is a spreadsheet?*
When the spreadsheet is first loaded on to the screen, only a restricted number of rows and columns are visible. However, what you see on the screen is really only a window on a much larger grid. In fact, many more rows and columns are available, should you need them. (Note that the labels of the columns run A, B,... Z; AA, AB,... AZ; BA, BB,... BZ ...)

Q5: *What sort of information might you put into each cell?*
Three different types of information can be entered into the cells of a spreadsheet: numerical data, labels and formulas.
Data
Either whole numbers or decimals (4, 170, 3.65) can be entered. In *Grasshopper*, the figures appear in their cells in *white*.

	A	B	C	D	E
1					
2					
3					

This is cell B3.

Figure 1

	A	B	C	D	E
1	Cheese	1.40			
2	Bread	0.70			
3	Eggs	0.75			
4	Total	2.85			
5					

entered as B1+B2+B3

Figure 2

Labels
These are words (the headings of rows or columns of numbers will be entered as labels). In *Grasshopper*, they appear in their cells in *red*.
Formulas
These allow cells to display the result of a calculation based on the current values contained in other cells in the spreadsheet. If an entire row or column of cell values is based on a single formula, it needs to be entered only once and then 'replicated' along the entire row or column. In *Grasshopper* the results of entering a formula will appear as numbers but will be shown in *green* (or *yellow*) to distinguish them from 'data'.

Q6: But suppose I need to change one of the numbers in the spreadsheet. Wouldn't that make other values wrong?
Provided the spreadsheet has been set up in a sensible way, its great virtue is that if one cell value is altered, any other cell value that is dependent on it (that is, referring to it by its formula) will be adjusted automatically. Figure 2 is a simple example of a (very short!) shopping list. The items are inserted as labels in column A, and the associated price of each item is inserted as numbers in column B. The total bill is entered into cell B4 using the formula B1+B2+B3.

Let us suppose that the price of eggs entered in cell B3 was incorrect and is adjusted to the correct value of 0.95. Immediately on making this change, the spreadsheet should automatically alter the total bill in cell B4 to the corrected amount of 3.05.

Using a spreadsheet in the classroom

Q1: What sort of use might I make of a spreadsheet in my (primary) classroom?
There are three main sorts of use:
(a) as a tool to support a *mathematical investigation* – for example, to look at the connection between area and perimeter of different-shaped rectangles;
(b) as part of a *statistical investigation* – perhaps to store and analyse data collected in a science lesson or on a field trip;
(c) *to help you, the teacher*, with keeping records of classroom information – inventories, records of pupils' achievement, and so on. Note that if you are in the habit of using a spreadsheet yourself, you are more likely to spot occasions when your pupils might find its use helpful! The case study on page 82 describes how one teacher, Stephen, only began to see the benefit of

using spreadsheets when he experienced it for himself by using *Grasshopper* to investigate data about the reading skills of his own class.

Q2: I'm not convinced that the pupils will gain more by producing a graph using a spreadsheet than by drawing it with pencil and paper. What are the benefits?

The main advantage of a spreadsheet over pencil and paper in graph work is that it allows pupils to focus on choosing an appropriate graph and interpreting its patterns and features, rather than on the technical aspects of how to draw it. The chore of handling data using a spreadsheet is the first stage of keying in all the data. However, once the data have been entered on to the spreadsheet, any subsequent analysis, including both calculation and graphical representation, is easy to perform.

Q3: What sort of issues need to be addressed when I start to use a spreadsheet with my class?

Here are a few issues which you may have to give some thought to:

- What is the optimum number of children around one computer when using a spreadsheet?
- I find it much quicker to enter the data on to the spreadsheet myself but I feel guilty that I am cutting the children out. Which is better?
- How can I prevent the computer-confident pupils taking over the data handling?

Getting started

In this section you are given basic keying-in instructions for getting started on a simple spreadsheet activity. Two versions are provided: for *Grasshopper* on the BBC B or BBC Master; and for *Eureka!* on the Acorn A3000, A4000, A5000 or Archimedes computers.

Designing the layout on paper

Some primary school pupils wanted to see which type of biscuit was cheapest to buy. They decided to calculate the cost of one biscuit for each type, using one brand of biscuits.

The layout they used is reproduced in Figure 3.

	A	B	C	D
00	biscuits	price (p)	number	cost (each)
01	rich tea	23	18	
02	chocolate	65	15	
03	ginger	30	18	
04	oaties	40	15	

labels

labels

All these are entered as data. Do not put any 'p's (for 'pence') in column B data, just the numbers.

Figure 3

78

Getting started on *Grasshopper*

This description is based on using *Grasshopper* with a BBC computer. If using a Nimbus, you may find some small differences in terminology and presentation of the commands.

• Load the program
Choose the option 'New sheet' from the list on the screen (menu). This will give you a blank grid of rows (across) and columns (down) on the screen.
Call up the choices menu by:
  F0 on BBC
  (F1 on Nimbus)

• Label your columns
Choose ENTER LABEL by selecting that from the menu (use cursor or arrow keys to move the coloured selection box then press <SPACE BAR>). Now move to A00 to enter your first label. Type in the name and press <SPACE BAR>.

• Enter your data
When you have finished, press F1 (or F0) and select DATA from the options so that you are now in the ENTER DATA mode. Now you can enter all your data.
NB: It is important that you do change from 'ENTER LABEL' to 'ENTER DATA', otherwise the spreadsheet will not work. The labels and the data should appear as different colours on the spreadsheet.

• Enter the formula
1. Move the cursor to D01.
2. Press F1 (or F0).
3. Select FORMULA, press <SPACE BAR>.
4. Move cursor to B01, press <SPACE BAR>.
5. Press / (this means ÷).
6. Move cursor to C01, press <SPACE BAR>.
7. Formula in heading (top left hand corner of screen) should read B01/C01 press enter.
8. To put FORMULA INTO D01 press <SPACE BAR>, move cursor to D01 press <SPACE BAR>.
9. Press F1 (or F0). Select COPY FROM SINGLE CELL.
10. Press <SPACE BAR> to indicate D01.
11. Top corner = D02.
    Bottom corner = D... (your last row).

Getting started on *Eureka!*

• Load the program
A blank spreadsheet should appear. Notice that the first row in *Eureka!* (and many other spreadsheets) is numbered 1 (unlike *Grasshopper*, where it is numbered 00).

• Label your columns
1. Using the mouse, select cell A1. Type the word 'biscuits' and press <RETURN>. The word should now appear in cell A1.
2. Now select cell A2 and enter the label 'price(p)'. As before, <RETURN> completes the entry. You should continue and enter all the labels in row 1 and in column A.
3. Now you can adjust the width of the columns to accommodate all the labels. Move the mouse so that the arrow cursor points to the black vertical line between the letters A and B in the headings of the first two columns. (Notice that the cursor has changed shape.) Holding down the left button of the mouse, drag this line to the right. Release the button when the column is at the appropriate width. Similarly adjust the width of column D.

• Enter your data
4. Enter data into the cells in columns B and C.

• Enter the formula
5. You are now ready to enter a formula in column D. Use the mouse to select cell D2. Type = B2 / C2 <RETURN> (Cell D2 should show the result of this calculation, 1.277777778.)
6. You can now copy this formula into the three cells below D2.
Select cell D2. Press the middle button on the mouse and select Edit → Copy.
Using the mouse, select cells D3 to D5 (by holding down the left button and dragging the mouse from D3 to D5).
Press the middle button on the mouse and select Edit → Paste. This should produce, for each cell, the results of applying the formula, giving the answers to 10 figures.
7. Finally, to reformat these numbers to two decimal places, select cells D2 to D5, press the middle button of the mouse and select Format → Number → 0.00. Press <RETURN>.

Using a spreadsheet in topic work

The case study in Chapter 1 on communication, which focused on first and second-class letters, was one in which the pupils made extensive use of a spreadsheet. Now might be a good time to re-read that case study. The case study which follows in this section is much shorter and is linked to the theme of transport. These two case studies provide some suggestions for spreadsheet projects that could be adapted and tried with pupils. The teachers who carried them out went through three stages in preparing a suitable investigation with their pupils. These are outlined below:

1. Theme

Identify a theme to work on: change, movement, water and so on.

2. Brainstorm

Have a class brainstorming session where different aspects of the central theme are suggested by the children.

3. Question

Pick one or more of these suggested aspects and encourage the pupils to frame them as *questions to be answered*. Experience suggests that investigations which are centred around a clear and interesting question are more likely to provide a purposeful data handling activity and one in which the spreadsheet will really come into its own.

Case study on transport

This case study shows how a spreadsheet was used by a group of pupils (Year 6) working within a large class project on transport. Various questions were generated and this group became very interested in train journeys and train timetables.

Below we describe how they worked through the **PCAI** cycle.

Stage P Posing questions

Figure 4 shows part of the topic web their teacher had used:

The questions which these pupils focused on were:
1. Which journey is the best value for money? (The children decided to compare various routes and modes of transport: bus as well as train.)
2. What is the average speed for each journey?
3. How much would it cost for a family to travel on each journey?

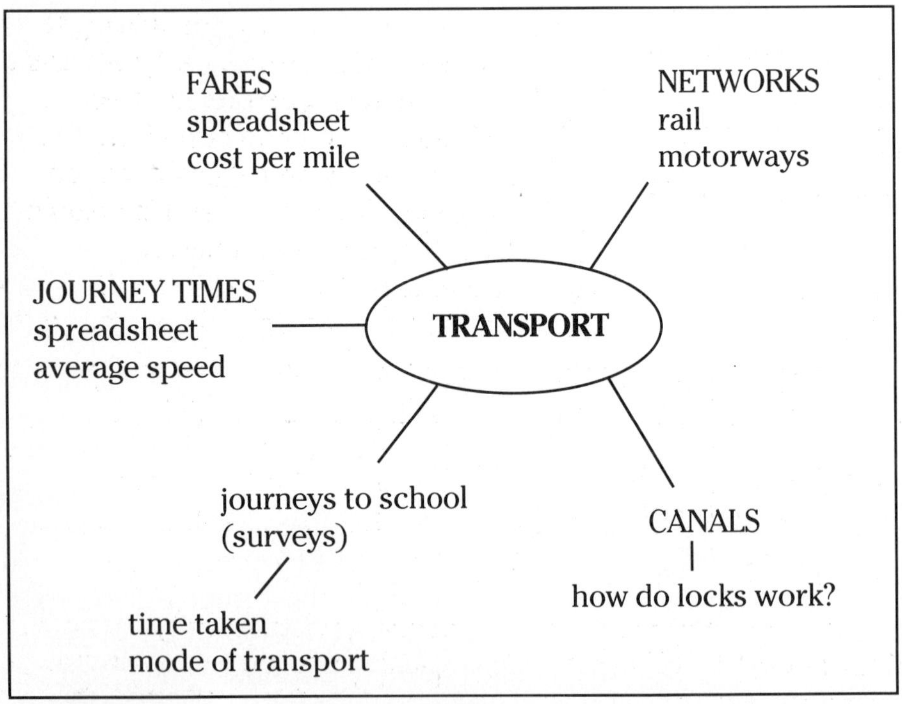

Stage C – Collect the data

The pupils used bus and train timetables, a road atlas and maps to find out some of the information. Details of fares were obtained by telephoning the bus and railway stations. The children had their questions written on paper before they started the telephone calls.

Stage A – Analyse the data

The *Grasshopper* spreadsheet was used to analyse each question.

FARES
spreadsheet
cost per mile

NETWORKS
rail
motorways

JOURNEY TIMES
spreadsheet
average speed

TRANSPORT

journeys to school
(surveys)

CANALS

how do locks work?

time taken
mode of transport

Figure 4

Figure 5 shows the spreadsheet layout:
1. Which journey is the best value for money? Which has the cheapest fare per mile? Decide whether to use adult fares or child fares.

	A	B	C	D	E	F
00	From	To	Vehicle	Fare($)	Distance	Cost per mile
01	Chester	Mold	bus	1.50	12	
02						
03						
FORMULA (in cell F01): D01/E01						

do not enter £ with data

Figure 5

2. What is the average speed for each journey? (Figure 6)

	A	B	C	D	E
00	From	To	Distance (miles)	Time (mins)	average speed (mph)
01	Chester	Mold	12	30	24
02					
03					
FORMULA (in cell E01): C01/D01*60					

Figure 6

3. What is the total cost for this group of people? (Figure 7)

	A	B	C	D	E	F	G
00	From	To	Adult fare	Child fare	Adults	Children	Total
01	Chester	Mold	1.50	0.80	1	2	3.10
FORMULA (in cell G01): (C01*E01) + (D01*F01)							

answer produced by formula

Figure 7

Stage I – Interpret the results

The pupils were able to answer their original questions from the spreadsheet analysis and went on to include on their spreadsheet a variety of different journeys as well as looking at other family groups (numbers of adults/children travelling).

Using a spreadsheet in the staffroom

This final case study describes how a primary teacher found using *Grasshopper* to be a helpful way of finding out more about the reading skills of his class. It has been included here to raise an important question about the use of new technology in education. This question is whether we can expect children to use IT naturally and confidently to solve problems unless teachers are seen to be doing so themselves. Children are more likely to respond to their teacher's actions and personal feelings than to their words, however encouraging these might be. Until teachers are seen to be using spreadsheets, databases and calculators as a valuable and necessary part of their personal and professional duties (and pleasures!), children are unlikely to believe that these tools really are useful.

The following extract has been provided with permission from the Centre for Mathematics Education, The Open University, and appears in the OU course 'Learning and Teaching Mathematics', EM 236, Unit 8, *Uncertainty in Data* (The Open University, 1992).

Case study – Using a spreadsheet to monitor pupil progress

Stephen, one of the teachers who helped the course team to develop the ideas for the OU course, teaches in a middle school. He felt uncomfortable trying to encourage his pupils to learn to use spreadsheets and databases when he himself wasn't really making proper use of them. The case study below describes in some detail how, with the help of a colleague, he began to exploit the spreadsheet as a professional tool which could provide insights into how the children were progressing with their reading skills.

A	B	C	D	E
Name	Chron. Age	Quotient	RA current	RA last
Tranjeet	11.2	85	9.1	9.7
Rajvinder	10.7	93	9.7	9.5
Nuala	11.2	100	11.2	11.4

Figure 8

Stephen now takes up the story.

'I heard myself telling the children that these spreadsheets were really useful but, to be honest, I hadn't found them useful at all. I had recently administered the Young Cloze reading test and converted all the scores into reading ages for each member of my class. Using the headings below, I then entered all the data on to a spreadsheet.

Name	Quotient	Chron. Age	Reading Age	Reading Age (last year)

Having entered the scores for the 29 children in my class, I printed off the data. It was a clear and well-presented table but I wasn't convinced that I had properly exploited the full capabilities of the spreadsheet. Together with another colleague, we spent some time working out ways in which we could use this spreadsheet more effectively.

The first difficulty was the way that I had entered the 'age' data, which was to record a child aged 10 years 5 months as 10.5. I realised that this was a misuse of the decimal point and was causing all sorts of problems. Not only were all the ages slightly wrong, but I discovered that the computer interpreted a

pupil aged 10 years 11 months (entered as 10.11) as being younger than someone aged 10 years 2 months (entered as 10.2). Clearly I needed to change all the age data to decimal years.

Another problem was the way I had entered the reading ages of three of the children who had recorded a very high score on the test and had been rated as >15.6 (i.e. a reading age of greater than 15 years). This was non-numerical data which I decided to change to 16 in each case.

I suppose these points seem obvious now but when I originally entered the data on to the spreadsheet I hadn't really thought through the various possible ways that we might use it. Figure 8 shows what the spreadsheet looked like after I had made the corrections mentioned above.

Our next task was to try to think of using the spreadsheet to highlight patterns in the data. How we did this was clearly going to depend on what sort of questions we were interested in finding answers to. After a short discussion, we decided that the main concerns were about how the pupils were doing compared with:
(a) their chronological age;
(b) their reading age last year.

I was also concerned to see if the boys hadn't slipped even further behind the girls in their reading and whether the Asian children in the class were performing as I

A	B	C	D	E	F	G
Name	Chron. Age	Quotient	RA Current	RA last	RA–CA	RA–RA(last)
Tranjeet	11.2	85	9.1	9.7	–2.1	–0.6
Rajvinder	10.7	93	9.7	9.5	–1	0.2
Nuala	11.2	100	11.2	11.4	0	–0.2

Figure 9

would like. Columns F and G were then added to the spreadsheet, as shown in Figure 9.

Column F gives the difference between current reading age (RA) and chronological age (CA). My first attempt at doing this involved carrying out the subtractions in my head and typing them individually as a column of numbers. However, my colleague pointed out that this was precisely the sort of thing that I could expect the software to calculate for me. So I started again, creating these last two columns as a *formula*. Column G shows how reading age score has improved over the previous twelve months. So, here I was looking for a difference of 1.0 or better in this column, otherwise the pupil had not been making expected progress.

Initially I had defined column F as 'CA – RA' (chronological age minus reading age) but later swapped the two around in order to produce results which showed a positive score for the good readers and a negative score for the poor readers. This was much more satisfactory and enabled me to produce more meaningful graphs later in my investigation.

The final version of the spreadsheet included two additional columns, sex and ethnic origin, and also a new row showing the

A Name	B Sex	C Ethnic Orig	D Chron. Age	E Quotient	F RA current	G RA last	H RA–CA	I RA – RA (last)
Alan	M	W	11.2	91	10	8.4	–1.2	1.6
Andrew	M	W	11	97	10.5	12.4	–0.5	–1.9
Carol	F	W	10.8	101	11	11.7	0.2	–0.7
Diane	F	W	11.2	8.4	9.2	9	–2	0.2
Fiona	F	W	11.4	111	13.4	12.2	2	1.2
Helen	F	W	11.2	86	9.3	8.5	–1.9	0.8
Javad	M	A	11.2	104	11.7	11.8	0.5	–0.1
Jane	F	W	11.5	100	11.3	11.2	–0.2	0.1
Jenny	F	W	11.6	92	10.2	9.6	–1.4	0.6
Jon	M	W	11.5	120	16	13.6	4.5	2.4
Lauren	F	W	10.9	106	11.7	11.8	0.8	–0.1
Lesley	F	W	10.9	110	12.4	11.2	1.5	1.2
Matthew	M	W	11.5	123	16	13.3	4.5	2.7
Michael	M	W	11	124	16	12.1	5	3.9
Mindy	F	A	11.5	90	10	10	1.5	0
Navtej	M	A	11.4	80	8.6	8.4	–2.8	0.2
Nuala	F	W	11.2	100	11.2	11.4	0	–0.2
Prakesh	M	A	11.6	96	11	11	–0.6	0
Najvinder	F	A	10.7	93	9.7	9.5	–1	0.2
Robert	M	W	11	105	11.7	10.8	0.7	0.9
Sarabjeet	F	A	11.4	101	11.5	10.3	0.1	1.2
Sandip	M	A	10.9	105	11.5	9.3	0.6	2.2
Sally	M	A	10.8	103	11.1	11.2	0.3	–0.1
Simon	M	W	10.7	92	9.5	9.4	–1.2	0.1
Stephen	M	W	11	82	8.6	8.6	–2.4	0
Sumita	F	A	11	90	9.5	9.2	–1.5	0.3
Tamsin	F	A	11.6	102	11.8	11.7	0.2	0.1
Tranjeet	M	A	11.2	85	9.1	9.7	–2.1	–0.6
William	M	A	10.9	102	11.1	9.2	0.2	1.9
Average			11.17	99.14	11.19	10.57	0.03	0.62

Figure 10

84

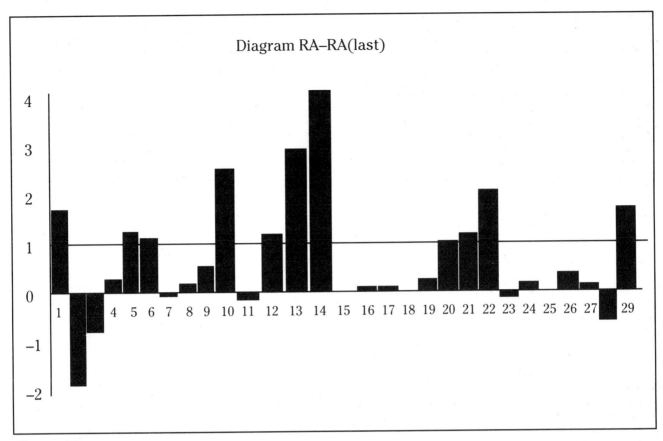

Figure 11

averages for each of the columns D to I. It is shown in full in Figure 10.

The row of averages revealed a number of interesting features, some of which I already knew about my class and some which provided me with fresh insights and questions about their progress. The average quotient figure was very close to the national mean of 100, suggesting that they were a fairly average class! I was reasonably happy that their overall reading progress was also closely matched to their chronological age, with the mean difference between their reading ages and chronological ages at only 0.03. However, I was very unhappy that the average figure in the final column of 0.62 was so much less than 1. Clearly, if these results were to be believed, the children had not made sufficient progress in their reading since last year. I decided to draw these results in a distributional graph to see how many children fell below the magic one year difference (Figure 11).

Drawing a horizontal line across at 1, I could see at a glance which were the twenty children who had not increased their reading age by the full twelve months over the year and indeed the three who had gone backwards.

Next I decided to look at ethnic origin as a key variable. Sorting the class alphabetically down column B had the effect of placing all ten of the Asian children first. (This is because they all have an 'A' in column B and therefore will be ranked before the white children who have a 'W'.) From this layout it was easy to recalculate separate averages for the two groups. The big shock for me here was that, as a group, the average improvement in reading performance of the Asian group was only 0.34 years, while the others in the class showed an improvement of 0.82 years. This was something that I decided to share with other colleagues and indeed it became a major issue in the school over the weeks and months to follow. It raised the issue of what exactly the tests were testing. We all felt that, in general, the Asian children in the school had a fairly good vocabulary but were less successful at sorting out shades of meaning of words in a context (which was very much what this year's test was designed to reward). So far we haven't come up with a satisfactory explanation as to why this might be but we have decided to do further research on all pupils' particular reading strengths and weaknesses and will try to put together a bank of remedial activities for those whom we identify as needing further support.

Colleagues agreed that this year's test was more difficult than the one administered the previous year. Indeed, everyone who did a similar exercise subsequently found that the improvement of their class's reading was under-represented by the test. However, a closer examination of the data revealed that the girls in the class had performed significantly worse than the boys in terms of their improvement in reading age over the previous 12 months. Here was another bombshell for the staff meeting!'

This ends the spreadsheet case study.

Many teachers have already used a spreadsheet as a tool to help them explore and analyse some of the evaluative data that are normally collected in school. As each year passes, schools are generating increasing amounts of such data. Having this information available on a spreadsheet or database makes it more likely that the classroom teacher can exploit it fully and gain fresh insights into important teaching and learning issues.

References
Grasshopper, Newman College, Genners Lane, Bartley Green, Birmingham B32 3NT.
Advantage and *Eureka!*, Longman Logotron, 124 Cambridge Science Park, Milton Road, Cambridge CB4 4ZS.
NCET (National Council for Educational Technology), Milburn Hill Road, Science Park, Coventry CV4 7JJ.

Chapter Six
Analysing data – Using a database

In this chapter we begin by looking at what databases are, and then consider to what use they can be put in the primary classroom. This leads to a discussion of the use of IT. We look at the important ideas of searching and sorting, and provide a number of ideas for working with databases. The chapter ends with some technical notes, examining particular difficulties which may be encountered when using computer databases.

What are databases?
Databases all around

We spend much of our lives collecting data in different forms – some useful, some not; some to be used again, some that can be forgotten. Many people keep personal collections of data, such as a birthday book, a telephone/address book or recipe cards.

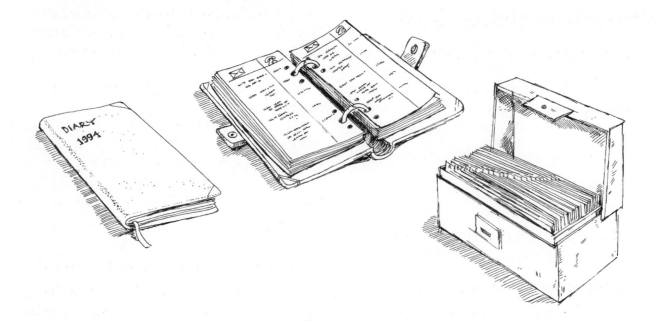

We are used to organising such data for ourselves and do not worry about how this is done, being happy to make lists or to store the information in specially-designed books.

The word 'database' has come to the fore with the development of computers whose memories can store lots of data. As a result, the electronic organisation of data, such as storage, retrieval and classification, has become an important aspect of data handling.

The information we collect may be useful for a single occasion, for example to answer the question 'How much shelf space do we need to store our sandwich boxes?' but unless we wish to recall the information later, or use it to answer other questions, we do not need to store it, nor do we need to create a database.

If I ask someone when their birthday is, with the intention of sending a birthday card in the future, I will need to store the information. I could just keep the name and date on an odd piece of paper. Alternatively, I may prefer to organise such data and put the name in a birthday book or make a note of the date in my diary.

Any personal database may consist of scraps of information, such as my pieces of paper. The information may be easy to retrieve, because I look through the pile of papers regularly, or it may be impossible to find. To help with the retrieval, I could organise the information in some way, for

example by writing it in a birthday book. The publisher has organised it by date and I only have to write in the names but for me, the book is useless as a database because:

- It is not up-to-date. I forget to put in new friends' birthdays.
- I do not think to look at it regularly to see if a birthday is due.
- I cannot find the book when I want to look up a birthday.

> **MORAL**
> Do not create a database if you are not going to use it.

For me, the information is better kept in my Filofax, which I carry with me. It can be cross-referenced to other data: once aware of the date of an imminent birthday, I can look up the address in the same book.

Computer-managed databases may contain similar data to our personal databases but enable us to:

- sort and classify large quantities of data;
- analyse the data to answer our questions;
- update information;
- store the information we have collected for a long period of time in compact form.

We can do all of these things ourselves, but the computer can manage them more efficiently.

Simple databases and computer databases

The National Curriculum recognises the existence and use of databases in the 'simple' and computer form, for example:

Level 3

Programme of study

'• entering and accessing information in a simple database, e.g. card database.'

Statement of attainment

'Access information in a simple database.'

Level 4

Programme of study

'• inserting, interrogating and interpreting data in a computer database.'

Statement of attainment

'Interrogate and interpret data in a computer database.'

The term 'database' in the National Curriculum is capable of a very wide interpretation. The example provided in the National Curriculum document under AT5

Level 3 cited above is 'Read off a value from a table; find the cost of an item in a mail order catalogue; compare the prices of similar items.'

So any ordered collection of data can be thought of as a database.

Most educators interpret 'simple database' as excluding the use of a computer. Probably the term 'simple' should be taken to imply the simplicity of the database and the use to which it is put, rather than the database medium.

How databases are structured

Databases are collections of data, organised so that certain information in the data can be found easily. In a diary, the data are organised by date. In the school register, the record of attendances is organised under names of the pupils.

Data in a database should be capable of being searched:
- for a particular item, or
- for sets of data sorted according to one or more criteria.

With the use of computer databases, a specialist language has grown up to describe the divisions of data entered on to a database. A database can be made up of *files*, each file has a set of *records*, each record is divided into *fields* (see Figure 1).

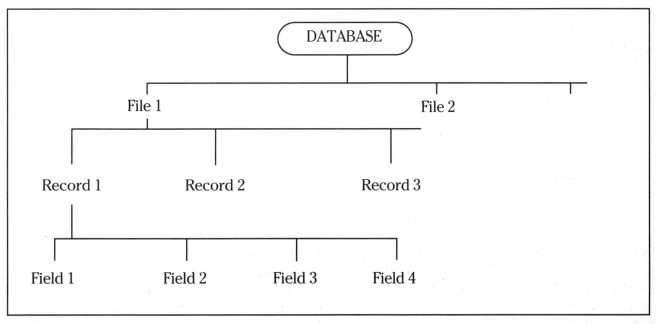

Figure 1

Some may argue that the collection of data cannot be called a database unless the files interact or link with each other in some way. However, much of the work we do in schools will deal with collections which are stored as one file, which for our purposes will be considered to be a database.

My address book

Information such as names, addresses and birthdays become recognisable as a database when entered systematically according to categories. My address book is a database, is simple to use and is not computer-managed. The data are organised into three levels:
1. It consists of one *file* which has been organised for me by the book publisher.
2. It has three *records* to a page.
3. Each record has space for three *fields*:
NAME,
ADDRESS,
TELEPHONE NUMBER.
　　Figure 2 shows some pages.
　　When I started using a Filofax, which is a database, I used the address section instead of my address book. The pages were set out similarly. The Filofax itself might be considered to give a better idea of a database,

in that names in the diary section can be cross-referenced with names in the address section. 'Dec 19th Mary A' in the diary section might prompt me to send Mary A a birthday card. I then look up her address in a different file – the address file.

Other data collections

Databases and data banks are often hard to tell apart, as the same data collections can serve different purposes for different users. There are many ways of collecting and processing data and sometimes the different forms and different labels confuse.

'A data bank and a database are both large collections of data; many people use the phrases to mean the same thing. Strictly, though, a database is a collection that is essential to a person or firm, while a data bank is a wider collection, more like a library.'

Collins Dictionary of Information Technology, Eric Deeson (Collins, 1991)

- The telephone directory may be a data bank for individual use, whereas for British Telecom, where all the information in it is vital, it is part of a database.
- In the classroom, the attendance register provides another example of a database.
- The library provides us with a database in the form of a card index.
- CEEFAX and ORACLE are examples of data banks which offer many of the facilities of databases depending upon the way in which we use them.
- Census data and returned questionnaires are also databases when collected together.
For our purposes, then, it is perhaps easier to consider any collection of ordered data which we want to use for recording, sorting, classifying and so on as a database.
NB There is now another common use of the word 'database'. A computer program for storing and interrogating organised data is properly called a database program (or package) but this is often shortened to 'database'. So database is the organised data or the program to handle such information.

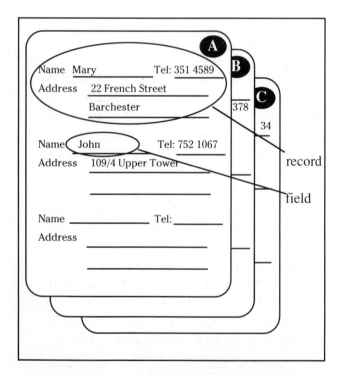

Figure 2: A page from my address book

How do database and spreadsheet packages differ?

With modern computer packages the distinction between database and spreadsheet is becoming less clear. Broadly speaking, a database package is used for storing, organising and interrogating data, whereas a spreadsheet package is used primarily to do calculations on data. The organising aspects are common to both, and indeed some database packages can do calculations. Database packages give priority to the data structuring; spreadsheet packages give priority to the calculations. See Chapter five for examples of spreadsheet usage.
NB Just as the term 'database' has come to be used with different meanings, so the term 'spreadsheet' can mean numeric data organised into a table or a computer program that holds such data and performs calculations on it.

What do we do with databases?

The PCAI cycle

In order to create a database we must collect data. If such an activity is to have any purpose we need to ask ourselves some questions:
- Why are we collecting the data?
- What need does such a collection serve?
- How are we going to use the data afterwards?

Children keep records of the books which they have read, and this information is, of course, useful to the teacher, and may be of interest to classmates. A record system for books read can include more than just the title and author – the answer to the question 'How enjoyable was the book?' is valuable information for pupil and teacher alike. A 'Books Read' or 'Library Books' database would be an asset to any class.

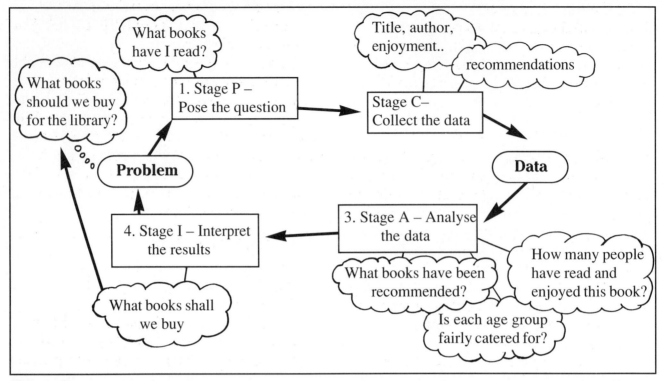

Figure 3

When involving the class in designing and establishing such a database, the **PCAI** cycle, which was introduced in earlier chapters, offers a valuable structure. Its application in the context of a 'Library Books' database is shown in Figure 3.

Creating databases can be time-consuming and boring if they do not provide something other than practice in creating databases! The reasons for collecting data are various, but some of the things we do with the collected data, our own or others, can be summarised in diagram form (Figure 4).

Planning a database raises issues such as:
- How are the data to be filed and remembered– paper, computer files, objects?
- How are the data to be selected or sorted?
- Will our selecting and sorting requirements affect the way in which the data are filed?
- How are the data to be amended?
- How easy is our access to the data?
- What questions can we ask and have answered?
- If we wish to present some information about our data, what tools do we have available?

Databases in the infant classroom

How quickly do we grow?

Put a sheet of paper on a wall, and mark on it at regular intervals (for example, at the beginning of every month) the height of every child. The marks themselves become the database.

Hand prints

Whenever the children are finger-painting, take a hand print, cut it out and date it.

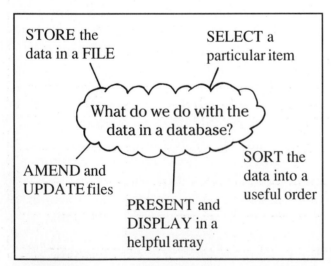

Figure 4

- Do their hands change?
- Who had the smallest hand?
- Who has the smallest hand?

Use the hands at the end of the year to make part of a display, perhaps the tail of a peacock.

What is the weather like today?

This is standard work for the beginning of the day – classrooms often have a weather board. It can be extended by looking at the weather at different times throughout the day, for example morning register, playtime, lunch time and home time. How will these observations be recorded?

Questions then might arise such as:
- It is raining now – will it be wet tomorrow?
- It is raining now – who brought their wellingtons with them?
- Will you need your wellingtons tomorrow?
- Will it be sunny for the trip on Friday?
- Does the sun shine every day?
- Does the sun shine every week?

The curiosity of the average infant and the skills of the teacher will no doubt lead to many more ideas, based on prediction, probability and 'the long run'.

Keep a table for recording some aspect of the weather (see the example in Figure 5).

- What happens over several weeks?
- Do you know in the morning if it is going to be fine at playtime?

Computer collection of data could probably be managed by using a machine with a Concept keyboard attached. The NCET have a program (*Touch Explorer Plus*) to allow a BBC micro to interface with a Concept keyboard for any program. A similar program for the RM Nimbus micro is available from IT at CSS, Martineau Education Centre, 74 Balden Road, Harborne, Birmingham.

Birthdays/monitors

Teachers often make boards showing:
- Today's birthday
- Today's monitors.

A table of relevant information might be made available so that a child could read from it (using the database) and then pick out the correct data for the 'Today' board.

Growing plants (suitable for Year 2)

The children could carry out activities to investigate:
- Seeds, bulbs, potatoes and so on.
- Which group's plants grow tallest?
- Which plant has grown the most during the past week?

Wet playtimes:
  Autumn term

Monday	Tuesday	Wednesday	Thursday	Friday

A more detailed record of the weather might look like this:

	Mon	Tues	Weds	Thurs	Fri
Morning	Heavy rain	Dull			
Play	Showers	Cloudy			
Lunch	Sunny	Showers			
Home	Sunny				

Figure 5

Using technology

How does technology help?

Before we create a computer database we need to ask the questions, 'For what purpose?', 'For whom?' and 'How will it be used?'

- What questions will the database help to answer?
- Can the activity help children learn to ask questions?
- Will it aid their discrimination of difference and sameness?
- Will it extend children's methods of sorting and help children to classify?

Why use a computer anyway? For a one-off lesson it might be better to use the blackboard or record the information on sheets of paper (or actually use the class of children as the database and have children supply information as needed!). However, if records are kept over several years the database would grow to be quite large and manual searching would become tedious and error-prone. Questions would not be asked (or not answered, anyway) because the effort would be too great. A computer database would be a more efficient, reliable and permanent store. If the data are stored in an identical manner they could be exchanged easily between classes or schools.

Computer databases offer ease and speed of access. Altering and amending files or adding extra data in commercial databases is often very simple, once you know the routine. Those databases available to schools do not always have the same power and severely limit the number of files, records or fields you can have, or may not allow you to add extra fields when you discover the need to store extra information. Because the processes needed to use or create a database are similar to those needed for any data handling and for aspects of sorting and classifying, it is useful to consider all these ideas as necessary stages in learning to create and use databases.

Computer databases and Attainment Target 5

It is worth noting that computer databases are very useful for reinforcing many aspects of Attainment Target 5 and not just those where the word database is found. A tour through Attainment Target 5 will illustrate this.

Level 1

Programme of study

'•selecting criteria for sorting a set of objects and applying them consistently.'

Statement of attainment

a) 'Sort a set of objects, describing criteria chosen.'

Of course the above programme of study is referring to a simple practical approach, not using a computer! However, this practical work can be echoed in later years using a computer database (and later Attainment Target 5 statements and programmes do that).

Note the plural 'criteria for sorting', rather than the singular 'criterion'. It is easy to sort objects practically using two (or more) criteria simultaneously, for example 'the *large red* counters'. The equivalent process using a computer database would require asking 'large AND red'. This is discussed in a later section.

There is some cause for confusion here. The 'sort' applied to the physical activity generally means pick out objects with common characteristics to form a group and so separate those objects from the remainder (for example, 'blue things'/'not blue things'). Sorting into several groups is similar, with each group having its unique feature (for example 'blue things', 'red things', 'green things'). However, the term 'sort' when applied to computer data generally means to rearrange into alphabetical or numerical order. A different word – 'select' is used to signify picking out some objects from within the totality of the database entries. The term 'search' is used to mean seeking out the relevant entries.

Level 2

Programme of study

'•choosing criteria to sort and classify objects; recording results or outcomes of events.'

Statement of attainment

a) 'Interpret relevant data which have been collected.'

Level 2

Programme of study

'•designing a data collection sheet, collecting and recording data leading to a frequency table.'

Once again, a practical approach is envisaged at this level. However, classifying is

an essential activity in creating a database. Deciding what the fields shall be and what form the entries within the fields shall take are important activities. Designing and using data collection sheets links in well with database activities, so this early work will be echoed later on.

Level 3

Programmes of study

'• extracting specific pieces of information from tables and lists.'
'• entering and accessing information in a simple database, e.g. card database.'
'• entering data into a simple computer database and using it to find answers to simple questions.'

Statement of attainment

a) Access information in a simple database.

Level 3

Programme of study

'• constructing and interpreting bar charts and graphs (pictograms) where the symbol represents a group of units.'

Statement of attainment

b) Construct and interpret statistical diagrams.

This is the first level where explicit mention of 'database' is to be found. This can be interpreted as either non-computer or computer-based work. The particular words 'entering and accessing' suggest that using a computer was envisaged by the authors but, on the other hand, the term 'simple' might suggest otherwise!

Doing the non-computer work first, followed by computer work, would be particularly helpful. Computer work at this level does not require the children to decide for themselves how to structure the data; a very small database with a very simple structure should be used initially.

Collecting the data is assigned to two pairs of pupils who visit the other classes. Another pair enter the data (supervised by the collectors). A class discussion then clarifies exactly what questions are to be asked, and a further pair interrogate the database to find the answers and report back. The analysis and interpretation is undertaken as a class activity. The second question is much more difficult to answer – it might be possible to find out who has moved away and link that with the parents' employment, but that is beyond Key Stages 1 and 2. Nevertheless, some speculation of this type is feasible.

Clearly, the database could be extended for other purposes – to include further information such as separate numbers of boys and girls, the age group, the location, special equipment (music cupboard, aquarium). This may mean starting again – it is not always possible or prudent to extend an existing database structure. A fresh start may be easier, quicker and better.

Example: class numbers

The local paper says the town is getting smaller. The class is interested to know if the school is 'growing' or 'shrinking'.
– Are there more pupils this year than last?
– Has the closure of the car components factory meant that people are moving away?

To answer the first question it is decided that the 'Class Numbers' database which was prepared last year should be updated with the 1994 data (see Figure 6).

Level 4

Programme of study

'• inserting, interrogating and interpreting data in a computer database.'

Statement of attainment

'a) Interrogate and interpret data in a computer database.'

This is the first explicit mention of the computer in Attainment Target 5.

	Field 1	Field 2	Field 3	Field 4
Field name:	Teacher	Class	1993	1994
Entry:	Mrs Bodeka	Y2	25	22
Entry:	Miss Rice	Reception	19	16
Entry:	Ms O'Ryan	Y4	30	33
etc.				

Figure 6

We create simple databases whenever we collect information and we use one in schools every day when taking the register. Whenever children collect information about their interests or enthusiasms, there are opportunities for creating databases. Sometimes we collect data, for example football stickers, creating a database in the book provided. Many non-computer databases which we use are not so simple – the library catalogue for example – but as technology becomes cheaper and more accessible it is clear that more of these databases will become computer-managed. In many cases our pupils are already familiar with databases; part of the teacher's role is to help them recognise these so that they can develop and manipulate their own databases with greater ease.

Having come to grips with the general principles by using a very small and simple computerised database, as suggested in the class numbers example, a larger one could be investigated. For example, the now rather ancient *Quest* database program, still found in some schools, had supplied with it databases on 'Horses', 'Planes', 'Children in Datchfield in 1881' and 'Weather'. These contain many records (from 55 to 168). Other similar databases are available.

Much larger databases can be handled by the powerful computers now available, which have not only much greater speed of operation but also much greater memory capacity. Both features are important, but for schools, ease of use is even more important. Database programs are improving in that respect too. For example, *Keyplus* has a 'Weather' file allowing pupils to compare the local area's weather with that in other places. There are distinct advantages to using ready-made databases for some work – they are tried and tested and extensive, and don't take an age to set up! The problem for the teacher is in motivating the work, and this needs to be done by setting up the situation with preparatory work so that the database is seen as a source to turn to for answers, just as one looks to an encyclopaedia.

97

Fieldname	Example	Notes
NAME	Avelignese	Commonly used name
TYPE	P	Breed type P – pony, etc.
CONTIN	EUROPE	Continent of origin
COUNTRY	Italy	Country of origin
HEIGHT	14	Hands: 1 hand = 4 ins
COLOUR	CH	CH – Chestnut, etc.
CHARACT	good-tempered	Breed characteristics l.c.
STRENGTH	sure-footed	Breed strengths l.c.
USE	pack farming	Most common uses l.c.
NOTES	flaxen mane and tail	Further details l.c.

Figure 7: example from HORSES file (168 records) for *Quest* database

Level 5

Programme of study

'• inserting and interrogating data in a computer database; drawing conclusions.'

Statement of attainment

'a) Use a computer database to draw conclusions.'

The example given is:
'Draw conclusions from census data about the effect of an epidemic/industrial revolution/change in transport.'

This is clearly a non-trivial investigation. If it is to be taken at face value, it really requires 'working backwards' by deciding what kind of interpretation of data will lead to the conclusion to be reached, and then deciding what information to extract from the database to achieve this. This is probably beyond Key Stages 1 and 2. Realistically, a more straightforward approach of looking at the data and seeing what they seem to say ('working forwards') could achieve the same result with guidance from the teacher.

Prior work at a simple level, as described previously, is vital for success in this kind of situation when wishing to 'read beyond the data'. It seems implied by the examples given that the database will be provided by an external source (such as Resource's 'Weather Studies' database) and not entered by the children (although in theory it could be).

To give an idea of just what records a database might contain, some descriptions of the *Quest* files mentioned above are shown in Figure 7.

Level 5

Programme of study

'• designing and using an observation sheet to collect data; collating and analysing results.'

Statement of attainment

'b) Design and use an observation sheet to collect data.'

The examples given include:
'Devise a simple habitat recorder for an ecological survey.'
'Conduct a survey of cars passing with one, two, three...occupants.'
'Handle data arising through experiments in science, geography or design and technology, or from published sources in other areas of the curriculum.'

The programme of study and examples here highlight a dilemma. Really, this work should precede the earlier 'Use a database' statement as it provides the motivation and purpose, and determines the nature of the data and the structuring required. The only sensible procedure is to adopt a spiral approach.

Example: Tree size

A class wanted to undertake a project on the size of the trees in the local park. They had to decide what data to collect and how to represent them in the computer.

A great deal of classroom discussion went into deciding all this. The precision needed to avoid ambiguity in the computer was an important consideration. What the children wished to find out had to be clarified in advance. Their main objectives were:
• to see if tree type and size were linked;
• to see if tree height and fatness were linked.
They decided that each record was to contain: Type; Height; Fatness. *Type* would be ash, oak and so on. *Height* would be 'small', 'medium', 'large'. *Fatness* would be the measurement in cm of the girth at 1m above the ground.

The teacher set up the computer database and a very small pilot run was made before embarking on the main data collection and data insertion. This was important to avoid a lot of wasted effort and frustration. This was not to say that problems did not arise. Deciding what exactly was a tree was never satisfactorily resolved! Identifying the types of trees proved troublesome. Measuring the girth seemed simple enough until trees with two trunks were encountered.

Example: absentees

The number of absentees from the class (or school) each day or week might form the basis of an interesting on-going data collection exercise, leading to addressing questions such as:

– Are boys absent more than girls?
– Are children absent more in winter than summer?

– Are absences large near the end of term (especially summer term)?
– Are there more absences on certain days of the week?

Such questions should not be imposed out of the blue by the teacher, but rather arise from classroom discussion. Also, they should be raised in order to test hypotheses, so that conclusions can be reached, that is, to gain useful knowledge of interest to the class.

There is further discussion about collecting information using observation sheets and questionnaires in Chapter 2.

Selecting and sorting with a database

Many of the activities using databases involve sorting data or selecting a particular item or set of data according to certain criteria. In order to be able to sort and select the data they must be filed in a way which allows access to individual items by using these criteria.

When children in infant classrooms sort objects, they are beginning to recognise aspects of sameness and difference inherent in those objects, and so they are beginning to recognise classification according to specified criteria. These skills can be developed and applied to data.

When collecting or using data, thinking about how you will sort or select items in the future will help you to decide on a sensible structure for each record. Data may be organised by:

• the use of keywords to identify types of data;
• categories within records;
• the response to questions.

Sorting is a routine activity in the infant classroom and many logic sets are available, such as people sorts, animal sorts, house sorts. These often come with cards or spinners and so can be used for games (which can help with probability).

Many of the early activities in the reception class use sorting according to one criterion, or sorting according to different aspects of

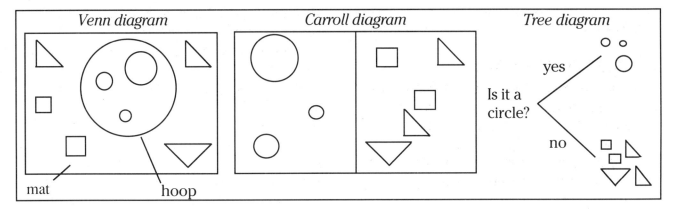

Figure 8

one criterion, for example sorting buttons into groups of different colours.

These activities can be formalised using mathematical diagrams. The three types used are shown in Figure 8, where the activity illustrated is a sort for circles.

Young children often find it difficult to sort according to more than one criterion simultaneously. The sorting activities given to them echo the way in which data are selected by a computer database: sorting according to one criterion and, once that picture is complete, re-sorting according to a second (see Figure 9).

Imagine a database set up to describe logic shape pieces. Keywords that can be used are easily recognised due to the way the logic shapes set has been designed: by colour, shape, thickness and size. Children can sort for red and not-red, triangle and red, and so on.

Children are also asked to sort according to the response to questions, using tree diagrams to highlight which routes they are following. The questions can be formed to allow yes/no answers so that they can relate directly to keywords, or more complicated classifications can be achieved. The questions may be used to identify particular pieces.

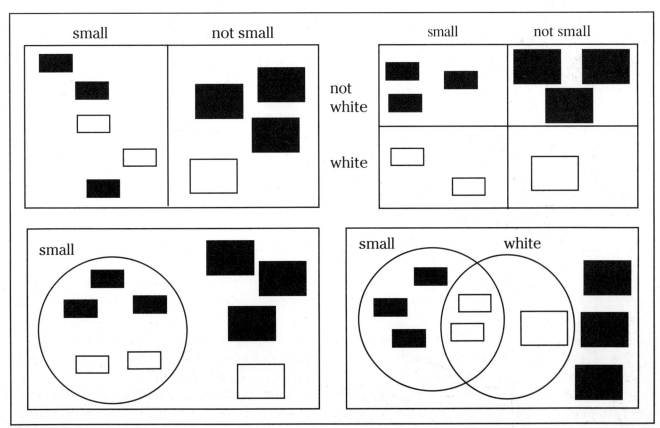

Figure 9

The two questions in the tree diagram (Figure 10) will identify four individual types of pieces:

- large circle
- small circle
- large square
- small square

The tree diagram would need to be extended with more levels and more branches if there were more criteria and more categories within the criteria.

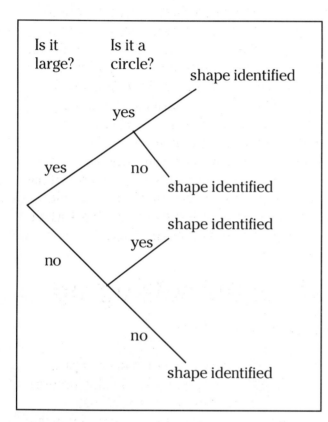

Figure 10

Note that one might use the small/not small classification, dividing all shapes into one of two categories. The alternative, which may seem exactly the same, is to use small/large as above, but really there is a subtle difference. The latter does allow (or at least hint at) the possibility of there being *more than two* categories (such as medium), whereas the use of the structure 'XXX/not XXX' is always confined to *only two* categories (a dichotomy).

The computer programs *Branch* and *Idelta* use data in the same way as shown in Figure 10, by allowing children to create a sorting tree. This involves the extra step of having to make up your own questions in order to create a device which will identify all pieces. Different children can create different trees, which allows discussion of the order in which questions were asked, which are 'efficient' questions and different solutions for the same task.

Another way of asking and answering questions is to use a simple questionnaire. Questions can be identified, and refined to create those needing Yes/No responses. This can be easy when describing objects you can see but may be more difficult in other circumstances.

If the database of questionnaires is created by having a card for each set of responses, these can be sorted semi-automatically if they are made into punched cards. A hole is punched in the card next to each question. If the reply is 'No' then the hole is cut out. If you want to find the cards which describe red shapes, the cards are stacked carefully, a knitting needle threaded through the first hole/cut, and the 'red' cards will fall out of the stack on the needle (Figure 11).

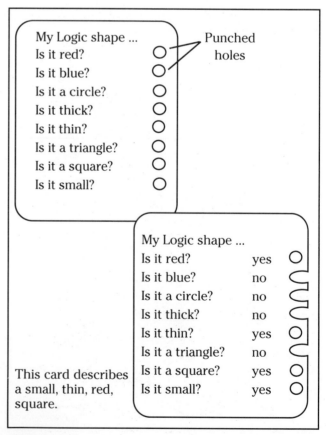

Figure 11

Sorting now takes on a different aspect, in that several cards describing an attribute can be handled together.

If all the possible criteria which describe the objects have been identified, a record card could be created for each piece. All the identifying features are contained within four fields: shape, size, colour and thickness (see Figure 12).

Shape	....	Shape	Circle..........
Size	....	Size	Small...........
Colour	....	Colour	Yellow.........
Thickness	....	Thickness	...Thin..........

Figure 12

A logic set is a closed set where all the members are identified according to specific criteria. The language of a computer database parallels that of these sets. The number of fields required is exactly the same as the number of attributes. Since logic shapes have four attributes, a record card (as in Figure 12) for any given piece would have four fields. The data for each piece could now be entered on a computer database, saving the data about the collection of pieces as a file, with a record for each piece (Figure 13).

FILE:	Logic shape pieces;
RECORD:	describes each piece;
FIELD:	one for each attribute (shape, size, etc.).

Figure 13

The software could then sort for each attribute, and tell you how many yellow pieces, how many red pieces, how many thin pieces there are and so on, just as a child could do, by manual sorting and counting. In using logic shapes to describe the different aspects of a database, it is not intended to suggest that they provide good material for databases. Logic shapes are for handling and sorting physically and an abstract computer representation is not likely to be of value. However, the example shows that the apparatus we use and activities we undertake with young children can be used to develop conceptual understanding of the structure of databases and how they are used.

Ideas for setting up databases

NOTE: these ideas are working examples but will not have any practical value unless you want to find out about the things suggested. The best database is that which is suggested by the interests and enthusiasms of your pupils.

Topic-based databases

Classes might like to create databases relevant to their current topic, where the work would take place over a limited period of time.

For example:
- What leisure facilities are available in the area?
- How do we care for the animals in the school?
- What do we eat?
- Choosing a pen pal.

See Figure 14 overleaf.

Database	Record	Fields				
Leisure facilities	leisure centre	name [1]	activity [2]	road [3]	town [4]	cost [5]
		days open [6]	opening hours [7]			
Animals	animal	name [1]	type [2]	description (e.g. furry) [3]	size [4]	food [5]
		number of young [6]	habitat [7]			
Nutrition	type of food	sugars [1]	starch [2]	fats [3]	protein [4]	vitamins [5]
		calories [6]	costs [7]			
Daily diet	name of person	cereals [1]	potatoes [2]	rice [3]	eggs [4]	meat [5]
		fish [6]	cheese [7]	butter [8]		
People wanting a pen pal	name of person	name [1]	address line 1 [2]	address line 2 [3]	address line 3 [4]	age [5]
		number of sisters [6]	number of brothers [7]	interests [8]	1st country choice [9]	2nd country choice [10]

Figure 14

Long-term databases

Other databases would be more useful if they were used and added to over a long period.

1 The books we have read

Each pupil could have a file, with each record being a book classified according to author, title, type (fiction/reference), topic, the level of enjoyment, suitability for ..., recommended to ..., length of text, pictures. A long-term study might reveal some interesting trends in reading tastes.

The database would also serve a useful purpose in helping pupils to remember the books used and might offer a way of widening interests if it could be made available to others who are looking for ideas of what to read. It may help to answer the question 'What books should we buy in future?'

2 Our favourite

Children are often asked to survey their 'favourite' food/colour/pet and so on. This information is sometimes sought only to provide data to produce diagrams, such as bar charts and pie charts, which will illustrate the choices within a class. A database of such information could be equally sterile unless at some time it is analysed to answer questions. It may be of more value to consider whether consumer choice varies from year to year. Favourite comics, cars, singers, footballers, television programmes and so on all provide data. If this information is sought in Year 3 and recorded on a computer database it

Database	Record	Fields				
Our class	Particular	name child [1]	address line 1 [2]	address line 2 [3]	postcode [4]	eye colour [5]
		hair colour [6]	hair length [7]	height [8]	length of arm [9]	arm span [10]
		length of leg [11]	head circumference [12]	hand span [13]		

Figure 15

might be interesting to see how this differs in Year 6, or in the intervening years. Do different age groups have different tastes? Would the information be similar in another school? Would it be similar for children in other countries?

3 Our hobbies

Children often have expertise in areas which are unused in classrooms. The database could provide a guide to such expertise and allow children to find others who share their interests. Over time it becomes clear when enthusiasms are short-lived or when they become the basis of a lasting interest.

4 Our class

Create a database which contains descriptions of every child in the class (see Figure 15).

This database could be more complex and be made up of a collection of files, with the data being collected in 1992, 1993, 1994 and so on. For a project on 'How we change' this could be explored using a spreadsheet. For example, using *Grass* enables the data to be transferred into *Grasshopper* so that numerical calculations can be explored. (Data recorded using *Our Facts* can be adapted to be used with *Grass*.) Some newer packages such as *Junior Pinpoint* combine the features of both database and

spreadsheet and so avoid the need to transfer the data. This ability to perform calculations on database field entries means that questions such as 'Is our height three times the circumference of our head?' can be investigated. An example of a data collection sheet for 'Our class' is provided in Figure 17 overleaf.

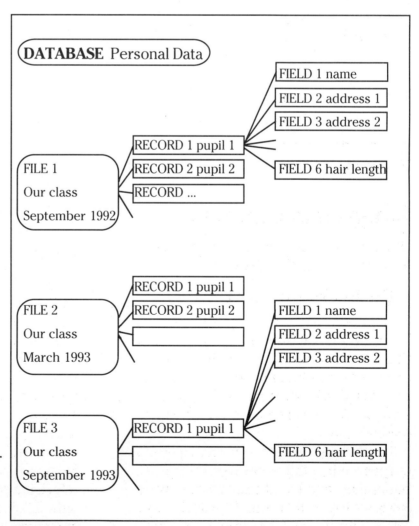

Figure 16

Our Class Database Recording Sheet
DATE COLLECTED:

Name _____   Height _____
Address line 1 _____   Length of arm _____
Address line 2 _____   Armspan _____
Post code _____   Length of leg _____
Eye colour _____   Head circumference ____
Hair colour _____   Hand span _____
Hair length _____

Figure 17

Once one set of records describing individuals has been completed, it can be used to identify a particular pupil.

If this exercise is repeated year by year, the children can see how they have grown and changed, a subject sure to interest them, and full of potential for data handling work.

5 Story book

Data could be collected and related to a story book, especially if other mathematics is being explored at the same time, such as enlargement or scale for example.

Story book suggestions:
The BFG Roald Dahl (Puffin, 1984) 'It wasn't human. It couldn't be. It was four times as tall as the tallest human. It was so tall its head was higher than the upstairs windows of the houses.'

Using the *Our Class* database, design your own giant.
– Would your giant reach above the windows of the school?
– How big would his house be?
– If a snozzcumber is related to a cucumber, how big will it be?

In order to answer such questions, extra data would have to be collected about the height of the school windows, the sizes of the children's houses and cucumbers in order to keep the measurements in proportion.

The Three Bears
When using this story it can be exciting to make or draw the objects mentioned. If each child brings in a teddy bear, data about the sizes of teddy bears can be collected.

Choose a bear to play Daddy Bear, one to play Mummy Bear and one to play Baby Bear.
– How big will their porridge bowls be?
– How big will their chairs be?
– What other data will you have to collect in order to make your decisions?

For other ideas, see *Starting Points from Stories* (NCET, 1993).

Building a reference library

An interesting task for older pupils is to build their own database which provides information about sources of reference. Many schools have a set of topics which are regularly used by particular age groups. Themes such as the Vikings, Food, Transport and the Egyptians are popular. Pupils are often expected to look up much of the information required for themselves. A database can be begun by the teacher and this allows pupils to find some information and realise how the database works (see

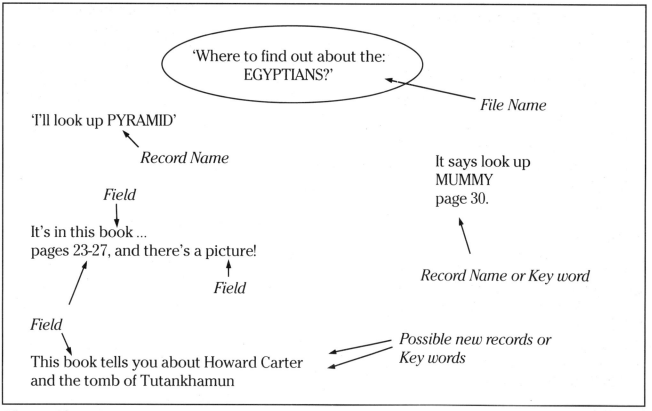

Figure 18

Figure 18). For example, part of the database might be arranged as shown in Figure 19.

Initially, the record on Pyramids may only contain information about one book, its title and author being recorded in field Book1, the pages to turn to in Pageref1 and whether there are pictures in Picture. The key words offer some other items which are mentioned on those pages and may lead to searches in other records to find more information.

The record, Mummy, may have another book listed, so leading to other information.

If a pupil finds another book in school with information on Pyramids, extra fields can be added so that the database grows. Information found, such as 'This book tells you about Howard Carter and the tomb of Tutankhamun,' could lead to the creation of new records. Over the time that pupils are working on the theme, the database will grow.

The next class which works on the theme will have a more comprehensive database, but the school may well have new reference books which can be added, or the interests of the pupils may consider different aspects of the information in the books already used.

File:	The Egyptians				
Record 1:	Pyramid		Record 2:	Mummy	
Fields	Book1		Fields	Book1	
	Pageref1	23–27		Pageref1	30
	Picture	Yes		Picture	No
	Keywords	Mummy		Book2	
		Tomb,...		Pageref2	
				Picture	
				Keywords	Tomb
					Pyramid,...

Figure 19

Imaginary data

Imaginary scenarios or databases might provide an interesting way of encouraging pupils to explore databases, but only when they offer a useful addition to other aspects of the curriculum.

1 Eye-witness

This requires an initial database to be set up containing data on imaginary children (such as height, weight, hair colour, eye colour), as outlined in 'Our class' on page 105. The database could be on cards or on the computer.

Present the children with an imaginary newspaper/TV report (Figure 20).

A dramatic rescue has been reported.

A toddler was dragged from
the river by a girl who ran away
straight afterwards.

Eye-witnesses are being interviewed in
order to find the reluctant heroine.

Figure 20

A small number of children are chosen as the eye-witnesses and they each separately provide some information about the imaginary girl (perhaps just one feature). As the eye-witness accounts come in, the children sort through the descriptions until they find who the shy person is. Conflicting accounts could make the exercise more realistic. This also provides a good language exercise as the children attempt to describe each other.

2 The Mathemaurs

A database can be created to give information about a 'mathemagical' set of creatures. A sample of these creatures is given in Figure 21.

Provide a set of clues and see if the children can identify which creature you have chosen. For example, which Mathemaur is hiding behind the ...?

Clues:
– There are three footprints in the mud close together.
– There are three eyes looking at me.
– I can see more than one ear.
– I heard it marching past saying 'left, right, centre'.
– It dropped four of its mittens.
  What other information is needed?

NAME	EYES	NOSES	MOUTHS	EARS	FEET	ARMS	HANDS per arm	DIGITS per hand
Binat	2	2	2	2	2	2	2	2
Triningle	3	3	3	3	3	3	3	3
Trinarmer	1	1	1	6	3	3	3	3
Bibiber	2	2	2	2	22	2	2	11
Octopeds	2	2	1	2	8	6	1	4
Pentabite	1	1	5	3	15	3	5	3
Icosadigs	2	1	1	2	16	2	2	5
Pentalook	5	1	1	2	10	9	1	2
Hexscoper	6	1	1	6	12	12	1	6
and so on								

Figure 21

The book *Wollygoggles* Thomas O'Brien (Jonathan Press/Claire Publications) is a good source for ideas for imaginary databases.

3 Write your own novel

In many junior classes, serial writing takes place, with sections being added over time. The characters and locations could be planned and recorded with the help of a database (not on a computer). The idea of keeping a record helps with consistency.

This is an obvious case of the database providing language reinforcement and, in fact, this is a common feature of database activities.

Published databases

For some software, such as *Key* and *Quest*, you can buy databases which are ready to use. More and more of these are being created. Like any reference works their value depends upon their use, but you may find many will fit in with topic work being planned.

Computer databases provide us with a wealth of easily-stored information, with ease of access only found in well-indexed books. With the development of technology they will include diagrams and photographs to illustrate the data. Hopefully they will become a valuable tool within the classroom, which pupils will use when they want to know something or when they wish to organise their own collections of data.

Important points on organising data in databases

Pets and pitfalls

Problems ahead

Here we will concentrate on bringing to the fore some of the difficulties which can be encountered if the teacher does not plan ahead or is unfamiliar with the way the computer database works. Although using database programs can be rich and rewarding, there are many pitfalls for the unwary!

A case study concerning the creation of a 'Pets' database is used here as a vehicle for highlighting problems.

A simple 'Pets' database

To record information in a database about the class and their pets there is an obvious way in which one might expect to structure the data:

Name   Pet 1   Pet 2   Pet 3   Pet 4 ...

Using paper and pencil this kind of database is fine. We just continue each child's list as far as necessary and no further. For neatness we would probably start each new name on a fresh line:

Louise   cat,   budgie
Rakesh   dog,   gerbil

If we want to see how many girls have a dog we can scan through the data, counting up as we go. As class members, we know which children are boys and which are girls (even if the name is ambiguous, such as Kerry!). The only likely problems are that we might miss some information, miscount or lose the paper.

Computer database – a first data structure

In computer jargon the complete data for one child forms a *record*, and each individual piece of information (Name, Pet 1 and so on) is a *field*. All the records together form a *file*. In this example the file might be called 'OURPETS'.

When using a computer database there are always difficulties to be addressed, and with the above example there is one in particular – having a list of indefinite length. Some children may have many pets, others may have none. It is normal for a computer database to require the same number of fields for each and every record, that is, every

record in the file has exactly the same structure. Generally this has to be decided in advance. For example, we may decide to fix the (maximum) number at four pets. This means that each child must have four entries. The entries can be blanks, but more than four pets cannot be represented. Also, we note that the computer will not know who are boys and who are girls unless we tell it, so we will need an extra field to supply that information.

The data might be structured and entered as in Figure 22.

Field names					
	Name	*Sex*	*Pet1*	*Pet2*	*Pet3*	*Pet4*
Entry 1:	Louise	Girl	Cat	Budgie	–	–
Entry 2:	Rakesh	Boy	Dog	Gerbil	–	–

(Dashes might be used to indicate no information.)

Figure 22

Once all the data have been entered, we want to find all the girls who have dogs. There are two approaches.
Either:
a) First use the database to select all the girls' records. Then search those records for the word 'Dog', and display all the relevant records either one at a time or all together; that is, display girls with dogs.
Or:
b) Do a search simultaneously using the two criteria 'Girl' in the sex field and 'Dog' in the various Pet fields (or in fact anywhere).

Some words of warning here:
i) Setting up multi-criteria searching can be quite difficult. (Note: this is called 'multi-criteria searching' because more than one criterion at a time is being applied.)
ii) Searching for 'dog' might, or might not, find 'Dog', depending on the particular database

and how it is set up or which option is chosen. If the data are not entirely consistent – which is quite likely – then some items could be missed unless the appropriate search option is chosen. Most databases can search for words ignoring the case of the letters (upper or lower case) but this may not be the default setting. This is something worth checking up on both in the manual and practically!
iii) When creating a database, specifying the exact format for the data is important, and checks on the data entered should be made.
iv) It may not be possible to do a search through all the fields in one go – it might be necessary to choose a particular field. In our example, having to search each of the four pet fields looking for 'Dog' could be tedious or complex. Again, this is something worth checking up on both in the manual and practically!

Computer database – a second data structure

The above was just one possible way to structure the data, and maybe not a particularly good one. An alternative is to specify in advance the type of pet expected. This would arise from class discussion or a small pilot study. Dog, cat, budgie, fish, hamster seem likely candidates. Additionally, one would also want a 'miscellaneous' category for the odd alligator. For example see Figure 23.

This has the advantage of having just one field for the dog category, so it is the only field which need be searched if one is looking for dog owners. It would be possible to enter in

Field names:	*Name*	*Sex*	*Dog*	*Cat*	*Budgie*	*Fish*	*Hamster*	*Other*
Entry 1:	Louise	Girl	Yes	No	Yes	No	No	-
Entry 2:	Rakesh	Boy	No	Yes	No	No	No	Gerbil

Figure 23

My Pet
cat   10
dog   8
Fish   6
tortoise 1
mouse
hamster
gerbil

We see here that Louise has one dog and one budgie; Rakesh has three cats and a gerbil. Now the database can store more detailed information in a simple manner. ·

You may feel that this is still not entirely satisfactory – suppose Rakesh has *several* gerbils or a gerbil *and* a mouse. Once again, the data structure would be inadequate. This is a fact of life – *no* structure is suitable for all circumstances. When designing a database one must think carefully about the raw data which are to be stored, the structuring of the data and the kinds of questions likely to be asked – all three aspects go together.

The difficulties which arise once one tries to computerise data only go to show the richness of situations in which data handling occurs, the variety of ways of representing the data, and the remarkable capability of the human brain for storing, retrieving and manipulating data. Any topic of the curriculum which addresses such matters must be important, which is a powerful argument for using computer databases with young children.

Two tough questions

To close this section we look at two examples of the kinds of questions which might arise in the classroom but which present a challenge to the teacher and, of course, the pupils. This may be because the questions are vague, complex, deep or impossible. It is the skill of the teacher to take such a question and lead the class to reformulate it into a question or questions which *can* be answered.

Peter says 'Girls like cats and boys like dogs!' Rebecca replies, 'That's not true because I have a dog.' Who is right?

Can we answer this using 'OURPETS' database? Not until the problem has been specified properly and it is known what to

that field either the word 'Dog' or '–', but 'Yes' and 'No' seem sensible. (A possible alternative to using 'Dog' and '–' might be 'Dog' and 'No Dog', but that could cause serious problems when searching for the word 'Dog'!) So, with this structure, to seek out the dog owners one searches the 'Dog' field looking for 'Yes'.

If Anita wants to know the answer to her question 'How many girls in the class own dogs?' you should note that this is not the same as 'How many dogs are owned by girls in the class?' If a girl has more than one dog then the answers to these two questions will differ. This raises the point that the data structure above can be improved. An alternative is given in Figure 24.

Field names:	Name	Sex	Dog	Cat	Budgie	Fish	Hamster	Other
Entry 1:	Louise	Girl	1	0	1	0	0	-
Entry 2:	Rakesh	Boy	0	3	0	0	0	Gerbil

Figure 24

search for in the database. And maybe not even then! Refining such vague statements into meaningful questions will involve much class discussion. Presumably one thing we want to know is if girls have more cats than dogs. That is much simpler and goes some way to providing the answer. The database can provide that information.

Lee wanted a cat but his mum said that girls have cats and boys have dogs. So he asks his teacher if that is true. The teacher then asks the class 'Are girls more likely to have cats and boys dogs? Use the database to find out!'

Such a question is actually quite tricky and more appropriate for Key Stages 3 and 4, but it may not seem so at first. (Interpreting the results correctly could be challenging if there are unequal numbers of boys and girls in the database.) It would have been wiser to have asked much simpler questions first – 'Are there any girls who have dogs?' and 'Are there any boys who have cats?' This information will answer the question at one level. Finding the actual number of boys and girls with cats and dogs and comparing the ownership levels for boys and girls (perhaps using pie charts) might be used to take it a stage further.

Pet ownership is usually a family decision (largely taken by parents), so pets owned by children may not be their own choices. This could be incorporated into an investigation.

Handling real data and dealing with real questions is bound to raise difficulties for the teacher, but also offers wonderful opportunities for language work and development of logical thinking. Skilful clarification or re-interpretation can do much to satisfy the thirst for knowledge but some questions will have to remain unanswered!

Representing data in fields for searching and sorting

Numeric and alphanumeric data

Computer databases can provide much information, provided the data have been entered in a way that the machine can handle. Information in fields can be alphanumeric or numeric. Alphanumeric fields contain characters (letters), special symbols such as commas, and digits. Often these are simply words and/or numbers. Number fields contain data in pure number form, with no units.

So, entering age as '11 yrs 6 mths' or as 'ten years' would go into an alphanumeric field, whilst '11.5' would (normally) be placed in a numeric field.

Handling numeric data

Data entered as numbers can be sorted, compared (matched), and the total, mean and other summarising values calculated.

Sorting numeric data
For example, the data:

11, 8, 7, 7, 10

stored in a numeric field called AGE representing children's ages, would be sorted into the order:

7, 7, 8, 10, 11

This is the obvious and expected numerically increasing order.

Searching (comparing) numeric data

If all children aged under ten were required, this might be achieved by searching the database using a statement such as: AGE < 10.

Similarly, to find all children aged exactly seven, the statement might be AGE = 7.

Handling alphanumeric data

Data entered as characters can be sorted and compared (matched).

Sorting alphanumeric data

For example, the data:

Smith, Jones, Patel, O'Rourke, Godino, Mistry

stored in an alphanumeric field called NAME representing children's surnames would be sorted into the order:

Godino, Jones, Mistry, O'Rourke, Patel, Smith

which is as expected.

Surprises come when the data have a mixture of letters and other characters, especially digits. It is obvious that 'A' comes before 'B', but does '3' come before 'A'? (Yes!) Also, clearly 'Ab' comes before 'Ac', but does

'8y' come before '10'? (No!) Comparisons are done character by character; when treated as *characters* '10' is *less than* '8y' because '1' has a code less than the code for '8'. The data:

11 yrs, 8 yrs, 7 yrs, 7 yrs, 10yrs

stored in an alphanumeric field representing children's ages would be sorted into the order:

10 yrs, 11 yrs, 7 yrs, 7 yrs, 8 yrs.

This is *not* the expected numerically increasing order, because it is not numeric data but alphanumeric data.

Searching (comparing) alphanumeric data

For example, to find those whose surname occurs in the first half of the alphabet, a statement such as: NAME < 'N' might be used.

Similarly, finding all those called 'Mistry' might be achieved with NAME = 'Mistry'.

Upper case or lower case?

Care must be taken to be consistent in using upper and lower case letters. Databases normally treat SMITH and smith and Smith as quite different, although there is usually a way to tell the computer that case does not matter. This can cause problems when sorting and when searching for a particular name. It is worthwhile checking up on this for the particular database program being used in the classroom, before children get into difficulties.

How many fields?

In sorting data, there need to be sufficient fields for each of the attributes by which one might wish to sort. If a person's address book were to be computerised, it might be nice to print labels for sending Christmas cards. As overseas cards need to be posted earlier than the others, it would be a good idea to sort for this before printing. To do this, each address would need a field showing the country.

Storing dates (not the edible kind!)

If the records of children need to be sorted to show children who are under five, one might ask for the file to be sorted for birth dates more recent than five years ago today, for example 16th April 1989. However, if the field has had dates entered in this way (in the sequence: Day, Month, Year), unfortunately the sort will not give us the order we want.

For example, given the following birth dates:

17th March 1989
4th January 1989
30th November 1988
4th September 1988
16th April 1988
11th January 1989

searching for dates after 16th April 1989 by seeking entries '> 16th April 1989' would actually lead to:

17th March 1989
30th November 1988
4th January 1989
4th September 1988

which is quite wrong.

The explanation is that, as was mentioned earlier, databases sort strings of letters and numbers as an 'alphabetical sort' taking the first character as the most important, then the second character and so on. So the data:

17th March 1989
4th January 1989
30th November 1988
4th September 1988
16th April 1988
11th January 1989

are sorted into the order:

11th January 1989
16th April 1988
17th March 1989
30th November 1988
4th January 1989
4th September 1988

instead of the expected and desired one:

16th April 1988
4th September 1988
30th November 1988
4th January 1989
11th January 1989
17th March 1989

The day of the month is not likely to be the most important part of the date. Normally, the order of importance is Year, then Month, then Day. We need to re-enter the dates differently if we wish them to be sorted by year.

One way is to re-enter the date as one number, for example, 17th March 1982 becomes 17 3 1982, becomes 17 03 1982, becomes 17031982 (or more simply 170382) becomes 820317 (reversing the day/month/year order). This gives a single number six-digit code which *will* sort correctly.

Another way is to use three separate fields – for day, month, year:

DAY (Numeric)	MONTH (Alphanumeric)	YEAR (Numeric)
17	March	1982

Alternatively all three fields could be numeric, with March replaced by 3.

The contents of fields and the number of fields have to be designed or adapted in order to allow the user to extract the correct information.

Once the fields are designed to give the type of information you need, then the computer will allow you to sort and count the data on file.

Calculational and graphical facilities

Much computer database software provides graph-drawing facilities, such as the drawing of bar charts, pie charts, scatter diagrams and tables, and calculations such as counts, means and so on. If much of the data collected are numerical, or you want to do lots of calculations on the number fields, a spreadsheet can be used instead. Some software acts as both a spreadsheet and database, for example *Excel*. Other software allows you to switch the data between both types, for example *Grass* (for creating and using databases) and *Grasshopper* (the related spreadsheet package).

As the software will produce diagrams of all types, whether they are appropriate to illustrate the data or not, the emphasis of the mathematics shifts from the drawing of such diagrams to their interpretation and suitability. For example, when does a pie chart give a better picture of the data than a bar chart? (See Chapter 3 for discussion on graphs.)

Conclusion

There is no doubt that using a database can be very stimulating for data handling work in the primary classroom. It enables a shift away from the technical aspects of handling the data to a more exploratory approach, and allows more emphasis to be placed on understanding and interpreting the data. For this to work, it is important that the database contains information of interest to the children, that there is a real purpose in having the database and that questions asked about the data are realistic and meaningful.

Chapter Seven
Interpreting results and drawing conclusions

Previous chapters have emphasised the four stages of statistical investigation described by the acronym **PCAI**. This chapter examines in more detail the fourth of these stages – stage **I** – Interpreting the results.

It is important to stress that completion of stage **I** of the cycle is not necessarily the end of a statistical investigation. Very often the results that are obtained and the conclusions which are drawn can indicate a wider range of issues that the teacher may wish to bring to the attention of the pupils. For example:

i)   further questions worthy of investigation;
ii) whether the results can be generalised;
iii) the need and wish to develop new skills in order to discover more about the data that have been collected and the inferences that can be drawn.

These points are considered in more detail in this chapter.

Further investigation

It is usually the case when solving an adult 'real problem' that the solution does not immediately present itself. Indeed, we may have to 'go round the loop' more than once before reaching a satisfactory decision. Furthermore, in real life, you have to live with the consequences. Often, when one problem is solved, another one is immediately created because of some sort of knock-on effect.

For example, a group of pupils chose to investigate how they could improve the school dinners. They came up with the following three recommendations:
• an improved way of allocating 'seconds';
• having a choice of first course;
• letting the sandwich-eaters sit straight down.

However, when these sensible suggestions were put into practice on a trial basis, some new problems emerged. As one of the children, Alison, commented: 'Because there was now a choice of first course, it slowed everything down and you have to wait in the queue longer.'

So, a feature of investigations with real outcomes is that children can see that actions have consequences and they can begin to try out the quality of their solutions. There may be a few surprises in store and perhaps some new questions for them to investigate. The teacher's role here is crucial, in encouraging children to monitor and evaluate the results of their investigation.

Generalisability

A statistical investigation into 'Facts about us' may lead pupils to enquire whether other classes are similar/different from themselves. Similarly, any conclusions pupils draw about themselves usually lead to inquisitiveness about other classes or pupils of the same age living in different neighbourhoods/towns/regions/countries. So, just how generalisable are their results? They may have found that most of the class have blue eyes, or that the most common way of getting to school is by car. Would the same results hold true in a city, in the country, with older pupils, in China? Indeed, how typical is their class of classes in general? What factors should they look at which might show up differences?

The sort of conclusions that they might make, therefore, need either careful qualification or further investigation.

The need for new skills

As part of a class project on Growth and Development, a group of Year 4 pupils wanted to look at throwing and running skills. They measured running times and throwing distances of children in their own class and also of a group of Year 1 children. In order to measure the running times they used their digital watches, which gave 'split times' to hundredths of a second. They could understand the whole numbers of seconds but most of the group didn't understand what the 'splits' represented. Without a better understanding of what their data meant, they couldn't make much progress with interpreting the information.

At this point in their investigation, a whole range of further mathematical questions about the meaning of decimal numbers arose quite naturally. Their teacher was able to harness the children's interest in the statistical investigation and use the context of running times to teach them about decimal numbers. First of all they wrote each running time on a separate slip of paper and attempted to order these times on the desk, from slowest to fastest. They then keyed the times on to a spreadsheet and instructed the computer to order the numbers. Finally they compared their ordering with the one displayed on the screen. Surprise, surprise! They were the same!

This example is one of many where a purposeful statistical investigation, which had caught the pupils' interest and imagination, made them *want* to investigate a particular mathematical topic. When the investigation was completed, the experience also provided a valuable point of reference when the same mathematical topic cropped up again. In this example, it was when the children were performing calculations with money. Their teacher was able to say: 'Do you remember when we came up with those split times on the watch? Well, they produced the same sort of numbers that we get on these supermarket bills. Look at this bill...'

A statistical investigation into leisure pursuits and pupils' free-time resulted in the following statement by a Year 4 pupil:

'The bar chart shows us that more boys than girls use computers at home in the evenings. There are more boys than girls in the class, so the diagram would look like that, wouldn't it!'

Such statements are not uncommon. It is one of the roles of the teacher to seize on such opportunities and encourage pupils to develop their skills further. The teacher concerned used this statement as the impetus to look at percentages and to introduce simple pie chart representations.

The fourth stage of the **PCAI** process can, occasionally, highlight weaknesses or flaws in the earlier stages of the cycle. Although this may prove disheartening to the children, it allows them to learn from their mistakes so that next time (or in further analysis) they

119

may see the need to be more precise at each stage, which means:
- define their question more accurately (stage **P**);
- seek out the most appropriate data (stage **C**);
- employ the most appropriate techniques of analysis to find the answer(s) to the question(s) posed (stage **A**).

Interpreting the results

Drawing valid conclusions at the end of a statistical investigation can sometimes be a difficult process. Pupils will often require the teacher's help, support and encouragement. Drawing a sensible conclusion will depend on accurate interpretation of the results of the stage **A** analysis (which is itself dependent on stages **P** and **C**). Figure 1 summarises both the four main **PCAI** stages of a data handling activity, and three key questions that link them together.

The common feature of these three questions is that they link each stage in the investigation with the stage before and ask whether the stage that follows is appropriate to the stage that precedes it. The teacher may find this framework useful in helping to evaluate pupils' data-handling work and in providing a basis for asking them supportive, helpful, encouraging and challenging questions.

These three questions are now considered in turn.

Are the data appropriate to the problem?

To find out if the girls are quicker than boys at completing a set task (for example solving a puzzle) it is not sufficient simply to record the time it takes one girl to complete the puzzle. In order to make the comparison, a second item of data (the time a boy takes to solve the puzzle) is needed. But is one pair of children sufficient? Which girl and which boy should be chosen? Should the puzzles be the same or different? Would data from six pairs of girls and boys be better? How should the time taken be measured? What experimental conditions will guarantee accurate results?

In an investigation conducted by a group of Year 5 pupils, the class collected data on a variety of physical measurements about themselves. On interpreting the results they discovered that the data were not as they expected. Several checks were conducted but the evidence appeared conclusive, until one pupil suggested that the data based on the measurements of Thomas (an exceptionally physically mature 11-year-old) had unduly affected the results. After much discussion it was decided that Thomas' data should be removed from the data set, so as to give more

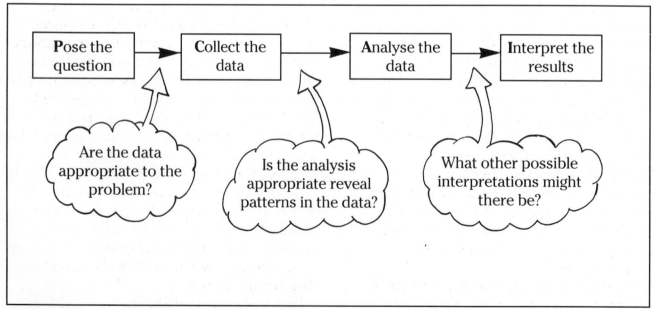

Figure 1

meaningful results. Unfortunately, the data collection process had not included individual names and Thomas' data were lost within the mass of class data.

This example highlights a common problem in data collection, which may only become apparent at the interpretation stage, namely that the source of each item of data may not have been clearly catalogued. Sometimes the children may choose to keep the sources of data anonymous in order to avoid embarrassment but they need to be aware that, sometimes, anonymity has its costs. Returning to the earlier example where a sample of boys and girls were timed at solving a puzzle, it is clearly essential that the gender of each test participant be recorded alongside the time taken, even if the individual names are left out.

Would it be appropriate in an investigation into 'Healthy eating' to survey only those pupils who have a school lunch or should those pupils who go home for lunch be included as well?

When the pupils on this survey began to collect their data, they were immediately stuck because they didn't know the answer to

this question. They went back to their teacher who prompted them to think about *why* they were collecting the information and what they intended to do with it. It didn't take them long to realise that the reason they were unable to proceed was that they had no real question in mind. They were simply carrying out a survey for its own sake!

After some discussion, they came to the conclusion that their central interest was about school meals and the sort of choices that children made – specifically, did children tend to choose healthy or unhealthy food when given a choice? This discussion proved to be time well spent. With a more focused question as a starting point, the ensuing stages of their investigation were not only more straightforward, but the pupils were now really interested in the outcome.

If children find that they seem to have collected inappropriate data, there are two possible remedies:
1) collect more (appropriate) data;
2) re-pose the question so that the collected data are appropriate.

Which of these remedies to adopt will depend on how committed the children are to

121

answering their central question, and how burdensome it would be to do the data-collection phase again. It is worth noting that, in the real world, the second of these remedies is not normally available in situations where the problem being solved is important. For example, imagine that you wish to shampoo your carpets and you decide to hire a carpet cleaner. Unfortunately, when you get it home you discover that you have collected the wrong piece of apparatus and have actually brought a cement-mixer. If you followed remedy 1, you could go back to the hire shop, collect the correct piece of apparatus and carry out the task as planned. Remedy 2 would suggest that you hang on to the mixer and spend the weekend cementing over the front drive instead.

Of course, no-one in their right mind would adopt remedy 2! The worry about adopting it in the classroom is that it gives the children a clear and unfortunate message about the arbitrariness of mathematical activity. The message implies that mathematics in general, and data handling in particular, are an end in themselves. It doesn't really matter what problem you solve or which graph you choose to draw, since their only purpose is to be stuck on a wall and be nicely coloured in.

This is definitely *not* the view of data handling promoted in this book!

Is the analysis appropriate to reveal patterns in the data?

At the analysis stage of a statistical investigation, the pupils will want to do something with their data in order to reveal patterns. This may involve one or more of the following:
- tidying up the raw data – perhaps into a list of figures, or a list that is ordered by size, or maybe even a table;
- using the data to draw some sort of helpful graph or diagram;
- making a calculation – perhaps finding an average or a percentage.

Two aspects should be considered when choosing what is appropriate at this stage of their investigation.

Firstly, is the technique appropriate to the data that they have collected? For example, if the children had estimated the height of the classroom door, it wouldn't make sense to portray this information as a pie chart, since the sum of the various estimates (representing the entire pie) wouldn't be interesting or useful.

The second aspect for the children to consider is whether the technique is helping them answer their central question. The pupils can easily produce a wide range of graphs and calculations, particularly when their data have been put on a spreadsheet or database. But, unless these techniques are helping them to come to a conclusion, the pupils are simply playing at data handling. There may well be value in such an activity, but it is probably more appropriate to do this at a different time, and not run the risk of losing the momentum of their investigation.

In practice, it is likely that children will need to use more than one technique at stage 'A' in order to reach a sensible conclusion to their investigation. It appears that the National Curriculum does not emphasise the use of combinations of statistical techniques as a method of analysis. Methods of sorting, ordering and summarising and so on are defined separately from, for example, construction of bar charts. This is unfortunate because often the most sensible and useful interpretations come from a combination of several methods of analysis.

What other interpretations might there be?

In an investigation into what the class did during the first hour after school, data were collected and summarised into the following broad headings.

Watch TV	24
Play on computer	11
Play games	9
Homework	7
Visit friends	2
Nothing	9
TOTAL	62

The obvious interpretation is that 'the most popular activity was watching television' or, at a more sophisticated level, 'more pupils watched television than any other two activities put together'. Such conclusions are reasonably valid but overlook possible flaws in the data collection and analysis stages. There are a variety of other questions that need to be asked if we are to interpret the data sensibly. For example:

- Is it likely the class contains 62 pupils? If not, why do the data show a total of 62 pupils? (Probably due to the fact that some pupils ticked more that one category.)
- What would the table look like if pupils had responded to the question 'What *one* activity do you spend most time doing between 3.45 pm and 4.45 pm?'
- Do you believe that each member of the class was given a totally free choice of response or were they restricted to the given six categories? For example, how would 'walk home' be recorded?
- What is the difference between 'play on computer' and 'play games'?
- What is meant by 'nothing'? Surely nine pupils were not held motionless and devoid of all senses in a time capsule for the hour!

It is important to stress at this point that, as pupils develop their skills in the area of data handling, the more informed their conclusions will become and the less likely they will be of making fundamental errors as shown above. This does *not*, however, mean that the types of interpretations and conclusions drawn by pupils studying at the early attainment levels are necessarily inferior to those with more advanced skills and experiences. Conclusions drawn by a pupil by sensibly applying skills at his or her level of understanding may well be as valid as those from a pupil studying at a much higher level. The key element, at all levels of expertise, is never to suspend one's common sense. If an average is calculated, children need to ask, 'Is this answer roughly in the middle of all the other numbers? If it is not, then they know they have probably made a mistake in their calculation. There are many examples of

statistical conclusions presented by secondary school and university students based on complicated analytical processes that the simplest of analyses (from Key Stage 2) would have indicated almost immediately to be nonsense!

Obviously, interpretation is a skill which will develop through practice and experience. In attempting to find an answer to whatever question was first posed, it is very easy for both children and adults to interpret the results by drawing the conclusion they want and overlooking other equally or more valid interpretations. Graphs and tables are powerful tools because they are helpful in indicating where relationships and/or patterns do or do not exist within the collected data. They can also be used as a means of making a convincing argument to someone else about why a decision or a judgement has been made.

Graphs are used extensively at all levels of statistical investigation both as a means of analysis and as a powerful means of communication. They are, however, the cause of many problems. Too often a carefully-drawn graph is judged on its appearance rather than the appropriateness of its use. Graphs should enable pupils to gain a better understanding of the data they have collected and so help them to arrive at reasoned conclusions about the investigation they are conducting. As has already been mentioned, many computer database and spreadsheet software packages include powerful graphics facilities which are capable of producing representations of the data under consideration, whether they are appropriate or not! The implications of this are that pupils can now spend their time more profitably trying out a variety of possible graphical representations of their data and choosing the one most appropriate for their purpose, rather than choosing in advance a (somewhat arbitrary) particular graph and putting all their energies into drawing it neatly and colouring it in.

Pupils need to learn that for every plausible interpretation of the results of a data handling investigation there may be several other equally plausible interpretations. By applying

and seeing a variety of methods of analysis, they will begin to develop a critical appreciation of the appropriateness of different types of graph and table.

Wider implications

If pupils are to find statistical enquiry interesting, motivating and enjoyable, the questions posed must be of genuine interest to them, accessible and relevant to their experience. In addition, and perhaps most important of all, the enquiry (or investigation) must have *real purpose*. There is little merit, for example, in conducting an investigation into ways accidents can be reduced in school if, when a valid conclusion or recommendation is reached, it is not acted upon. This can, of course, cause some difficulties, but it is not impossible to achieve.

An earlier chapter described an investigation into postal delivery times. In this activity pupils posed their own question and, with the support of their teacher, designed their own methods of data-collection and analysis. It is obvious from the report that the pupils were

actively involved at *all* stages of the investigation and therefore found the activity of interest, enjoyable and, of course, motivating. So what purpose was there to the activity? The original 'posed question' was formulated by the pupils themselves and was therefore motivating to them simply because of that. The teacher also reported that the pupils decided to share their results with the Post Office authority, and it is this action which gave increased (or what might be called *value-added*) purpose to the activity. Even more value-added purpose would be generated if the relevant postal authority comes back to the pupils with a thoughtful reply which demonstrates that it has taken their investigation seriously.

It is therefore important at the first stages of a statistical investigation to consider for what purpose the investigation is being conducted and whether there can be some sort of 'action outcome' for the pupils, once a conclusion is reached. Projects which have action outcomes are not always the most popular in schools, least of all with other colleagues, the head teacher and the school caretaker! Sometimes they will open a can of worms that you may have preferred to have kept tightly sealed.

Here are three examples of classroom investigations which may have wider implications for the rest of the school, and which will raise practical problems if they are to be implemented.

Investigation 1: Our week at school

If a class concluded, for example, that they would prefer the regime of a more formal or structured weekly timetable (perhaps mathematics after break-time on Mondays, Wednesdays and Fridays) would you (could you) implement such a timetable? Who would design the new timetable?

Investigation 2: Lunchtime arrangements

If, as a year group, Year 3 pupils concluded that Years 1, 2 and 3 would benefit from a minor alteration to the school day (e.g. being allowed to bring forward their lunch period by five minutes to avoid older pupils 'pushing-in'), would you (could you) implement such a change?

Investigation 3: School uniform

If the result of a whole-school survey revealed that there was overwhelming enthusiasm for a change in school policy on uniform, would you (could you) approach the head teacher, governors and parents so that such a change could be implemented?

It was just such a school uniform survey in a Doncaster school that resulted (after further consultations) in the implementation of a general school uniform policy. Traditionally, the school had a *no school uniform* policy, but within two years of the original pupil survey a two-colour school uniform was being worn by all pupils.

Purposeful activities stimulate interest and motivation. If pupils are given the opportunity to collect and analyse for themselves real data related to issues in which they themselves initially expressed an interest, they will begin to regard data handling as a useful tool which can be put to good use in many different areas of their studies and as a means of tackling problems in their everyday lives. Maintaining this enthusiasm will require teachers to ensure that the investigations are *not* regarded as trivial, but have real purpose and that when conclusions are reached they are, as far as possible and appropriate, acted upon.

Further reading

Practical Data Handling in the National Curriculum for Mathematics (Book 1) Glyn Davies (Hodder & Stoughton, 1993)
Supporting Primary Mathematics PM649, Handling Data, Alan Graham (Open University Press, 1990)

Chapter Eight
Probability

The topic of probability is concerned with judging how likely something is to happen and trying to measure this. Probability helps us to predict the future on the basis of past experience, and to avoid being taken in by strange coincidences. For example, how surprised should you be if you toss a coin and get heads five times in a row? What are the chances of a sixth toss landing heads, given that the first five have also been heads?

Probability all around us

Probability is not only of concern in the artificial world of dice, coins, cards, and so on. Chance events are all around us – indeed most events have a degree of uncertainty. We survive and cope by learning which events have low probability and which have high probability. Statements based on probability abound:

'Don't do that – you might hurt yourself!'
'I bet the teacher will be cross with you!'
'You were lucky, I'll beat you next time!'
'I expect Jonathan will be late again today'.

Chance happenings can be common or rare. Most days some letters are delivered, but there are *never* any on Sundays. The school bus *usually* arrives to collect the children. The electricity supply is *rarely* disrupted. Fire is a serious danger to a school and its inhabitants but the *risk is very low*

enables people to judge the significance of differences between sets of data. For example, if on a reading test the boys' average is 62 and the girls' is 64, should we conclude that the girls are better at reading?

Probability by no means need be restricted to statistical analysis of games. Here is what a teacher wrote about a local history study with Year 6 children.

'Probability has a language element. I have used parish records for this purpose when looking at baptisms, marriages and burials.

Jan 1821 Hannah _____ baptised

The children trace this child if possible to see if they can find when she died. In this way age-spans, for say the first 100 people baptised in a particular year, can be recorded and life expectancy worked out. This may then be steered towards discussion of probabilities.

What are the chances of living to age 1?
What are the chances of living to age 5?
What are the chances of living to age 15?
.... and so on.

Can this be plotted on a probability scale? It is important that children work in groups, or at least with a partner, although, provided the number of records is quite small and information pooled, my experience is that they thoroughly enjoyed this piece of detective work. My emphasis is on discussion and introducing the idea of a probability scale.'

In this section, we discuss the introduction of probability as part of the National Curriculum at Levels 1 to 6. This material may be unfamiliar to many teachers, as probability has not traditionally been part of the primary mathematics curriculum.

More than in any other area of mathematics, the definitions and terminology of probability are open to different interpretations and are difficult to get across in a chapter such as this. It is not easy to be precise without sounding pedantic or abstruse.

because we take precautions. An earthquake is *so unlikely* that we dismiss it as a possibility. Minor accidents – cuts and bruises – are *common* and we keep a first-aid kit. We don't keep an ambulance on stand-by at school, but there are a lot at a Formula One Grand Prix.

Probability in the classroom

At school, the teacher can draw on the children's experience and build on it. Discussions can set the scene for practical work by raising questions which require experiments to provide data for analysis and interpretation – the familiar **PCAI** cycle. Games provide interesting scenarios for children to explore. Why does the player going first usually win? How do we know this is a fair game?

At a more advanced level, probability helps when comparing two or more sets of data, to examine whether the differences between them are due to chance variation or to a real underlying difference between them. This

Level 1

Programme of study
'• Recognising possible outcomes of
random events.'

An example of a possible activity based on
this would be predicting whether the next
vehicle to come along the road might be:
(a) a car, a bus, a lorry;
(b) red, blue, black;
(c) travelling slowly, at normal speed, fast;
(d) driven by my mum, not driven by my mum;
(e) bearing year registration letter A, B, C;
(f) stolen, not stolen;
(g) carrying 1, 2, 3, people;
(h) moving.

Young children do not always find it easy to
determine what the valid outcomes are. For
example, a teacher put ten black counters and
five white counters in a cloth bag and shook
them up. She asked Daniel to predict what
would be picked out, hoping for an erudite
response. Peter responded 'Red!' When the
teacher asked him why he had said this, he
replied 'Because I like red'. Peter, like many
young children, had difficulty in
distinguishing the possible from the
impossible; reality and fantasy are not so
different for him; what is desired is what is
expected. This Level 1 programme of study
relates very closely to Level 2, since deciding
what are the possible outcomes and knowing
that an outcome is impossible are interlinked.

Events and outcomes

The words *event* and *outcome* have particular
meanings, but in text books they are often
used very loosely. We suggest that they are
used in the following way.

An *event* describes a particular situation
which has one, or usually several, possible
outcomes. Normally the particular *outcome*
cannot be predicted in advance. The
distinction between an event and its possible
outcomes can be made clear by considering
the following examples concerning a letter
pushed through the letterbox. Three events
are considered: first, the way it lands; second,
to whom it is addressed; and third, whether it
was posted first-class (Figure 1).

A *random* event is one where the outcome
cannot be predicted.

Everyday classroom life is full of random
events, which can be profitably discussed
with the children. The discussion can be
focused on making sure that children realise
that the situation is uncertain and helping

Event	Possible outcomes
How the letter lands on the mat	1. It is face up. 2. It is face down.
To whom it is addressed (first person named if joint)	1. Mum 2. Dad 3. Sandra 4. Peter 5. Someone else or unspecified
Whether sent first-class	1. First-class 2. NOT first-class

Figure 1

them to determine the possible outcomes. For instance, we may ask 'What do you think the weather will be like tomorrow?'

Some possible questions for discussion (at appropriate times of the year) are:
- Who will be absent tomorrow?
- Will Liam, who caught measles yesterday, be here tomorrow?
- Will it be raining this time tomorrow?
- Will the new addition to Sian's family be a girl?
- Will we have heavy snow in the middle of our summer holidays in Tenerife?
- Will I receive presents on Christmas Day?
- Will we be lying on the beach at Southend, sunning ourselves, on Christmas Day?
- Will I (the teacher) be present in school tomorrow?

Even in Tenerife it is (just) conceivable that there will be snow in midsummer, but the probability is so tiny that for practical purposes it might be classified as impossible.

All the above examples concern future events. This is the most appropriate setting, but not strictly necessary. For example, you could consider the statement: 'There was a day last year when precisely six children were away from school'. This is either true or false and, since we don't know which, a probability could be assigned based on our experience, just as we could assign a probability for the future event: 'There will be a day next year when precisely six children are away from school.' Such instances are philosophically difficult, and may be best avoided!

Certain, uncertain and impossible outcomes

Level 2

Programme of study
'• Recognise that there is a degree of uncertainty about the outcome of some events but that others are either certain or impossible.'

Statement of attainment
'Recognising that there is a degree of uncertainty about the outcomes of some events and that other events are either certain or impossible.'

Some outcomes of the events described above are *certain* or almost certain: it is almost certain that Liam will still have measles tomorrow, so will not be here in school, if he only caught the illness yesterday.

Some outcomes of events are classified as *impossible*: Sian's mother may have twins, or even quintuplets, but we say it is impossible that she will have 20 babies at the same time. In ordinary conversation the term impossible can mean many things:
'It's impossible for me to come to see you,' meaning 'It's difficult.'
'It's impossible for the headteacher to discuss this matter with you, Mrs Brown,' meaning 'It's forbidden, or unethical.'
'Agassi just did the impossible in returning that ball into the court,' meaning 'It was amazing'.

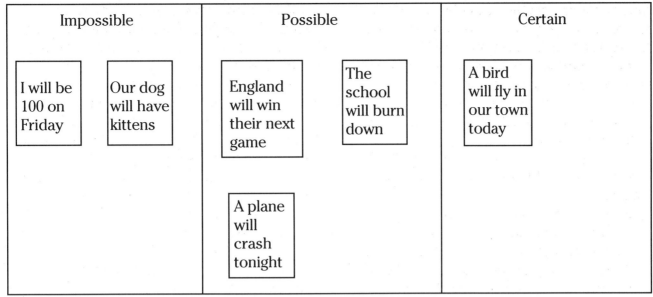

Figure 2

Only the last of these (Agassi's return) has a ready interpretation in terms of probability – it was *very unlikely*. The distinction between the truly impossible and the very unlikely is a fine one in practice.

Some outcomes of events are classified as *uncertain*: it is uncertain whether it will be raining this time tomorrow, or whether the new baby in Sian's family will be a girl, or whether the school will be hit by lightning today.

Children can be asked to make up their own events, and to decide whether the outcomes are certain, possible or impossible. This can help develop language and is more active than simply asking children to respond to statements presented to them.

Example

Event: Ian's height in ten year's time.
Outcome may be: Ian will be taller than 10 metres.
This outcome is *impossible*.
Outcome may be: Ian will be taller than 1 metre 80 centimetres.
This outcome is *possible*.

Possible follow-up activities include sorting sets of cards which describe the outcomes of events into sets of certain, uncertain and impossible outcomes (see Figure 2).

This could be used as a display, with children adding to it themselves over a period of time.

'Evens'

Level 3

Programmes of study:

'• Placing events in order of 'likelihood' and using appropriate words to identify the chance.'
'• Understanding and using the idea of 'evens' and saying whether events are more or less likely than this.'
'• Distinguishing between 'fair' and 'unfair.'

Statement of attainment:

'Use appropriate language to justify decisions when placing events in order of 'likelihood.''

As we can see from the questionable wording of the statement of attainment, people often say 'event' when they mean the 'outcome of an event'. At this level, children should be encouraged to discriminate between more likely outcomes and less likely outcomes. For example, on the first day of term, the outcome of the event 'the school will be open tomorrow' is very nearly certain, but not absolutely certain; there might be an arson attack in the night. The event 'tomorrow's weather' is fairly likely to have the outcome 'wet' when the forecast has predicted wet weather for tomorrow.

In general, the event 'the teacher will be absent tomorrow' is unlikely to have the outcome 'yes'. However, if it is known that the teacher was knocked down by a bus on the way to school this morning, then the outcome is very likely to be 'yes'. This kind of complication can make probability a difficult topic to talk about. Assumptions have to be made about which factors are to be taken into account and which are to be ignored. This can cause confusion, disagreement and misunderstanding.

Children can be asked to place cards such as 'It will be wet tomorrow' at appropriate places on a line labelled as shown in Figure 3, and to justify their choices of position.

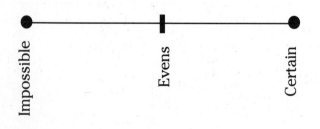

Figure 3

Some outcomes of an event are about as likely as they are unlikely. The new addition to Sian's family is about as likely to be a girl as it is to be a boy (based on previous experience); a letter posted through a door is as likely to land face up as face down (based on our ignorance of any factor which would suggest otherwise). The wording 'evens' can be used to describe such situations, and can be added to the labelling on the line as in Figure 4. Children should now try to place their cards on the correct side of the 'evens' point.

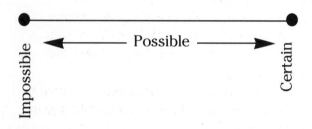

Figure 4

Some teachers have found it helpful to use a 'washing-line' and pegs to hang up statements in the various positions (Figure 5).

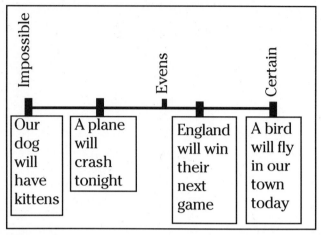

Figure 5

Just because there are two possible outcomes does not mean that these are necessarily about equally likely. Far fewer letters are sent first-class than second-class; more drawing pins land point down than point up when a packet is emptied on to a table.

Dice manufacturers do their best to produce *fair* dice, which have equal chances of landing on each face. From educational suppliers, it is possible to obtain loaded, or *unfair*, dice, which have been weighted behind one spot with a lump of lead. For example, the Mathematical Association sell dice heavily loaded towards 6 (and others towards 1). The teacher should keep careful track of the whereabouts of these dice! A game of chance is said to be 'fair' if every player has an equal chance of winning. Children can test the fairness of a die by throwing it many times. However, unless a die is heavily loaded, the number of times needed to test for its fairness must be very large – in the hundreds, rather than the tens.

The terms 'evens' and '50–50' are often used very loosely without proper understanding. They are a particular instance of the concept of 'equally likely', when there are just two possible outcomes. The most obvious example is the outcome of tossing a coin. There is a tendency for children to treat any event with two outcomes as equivalent to this, even though the two probabilities differ.

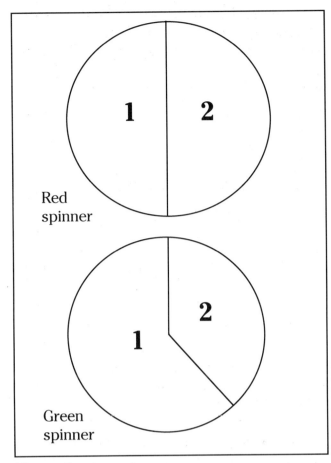

Red
spinner

Green
spinner

Figure 6

For example:
- The red spinner has a 1 and a 2. What are the chances of getting a 1?
- The green spinner has a 1 and a 2. What are the chances of getting a 1? (see Figure 6)

The words 'fair' and 'unfair' are well established in children's vocabularies, and their keen interest in fairness can be a stimulus to good work in probability. Games which are or are not fair can be investigated and discussed. However, children's ideas of 'fairness' may have more to do with ethical or moral correctness or personal benefit than equal likelihood, so there is the potential for confusion here.

Case study – shopping

As another reminder that probability work can pervade the whole curriculum at all levels, we report what a teacher did as part of a Key Stage 1 project on Shopping.

Shopping

As part of a topic on Shops and shopping (see Figure 7 overleaf) we began with a class discussion of shops which the children might see in a shopping street (two examples of the children's written work are provided overleaf). Questions raised included:
- Which shops will *certainly* be in the street?
- Which shops will be *impossible* to see in the street?
- Which shops will be *uncertain* to be found in the street?

As these three terms – certain, impossible uncertain – are limited, it soon became apparent that they needed refining, so more vocabulary in terms of 'more likely', 'less likely' was introduced, in this case shifting naturally from Level 2 to Level 3 work.

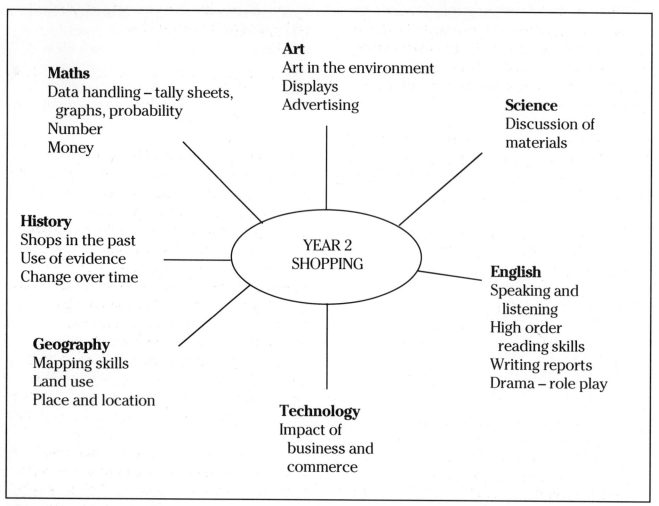

Figure 7

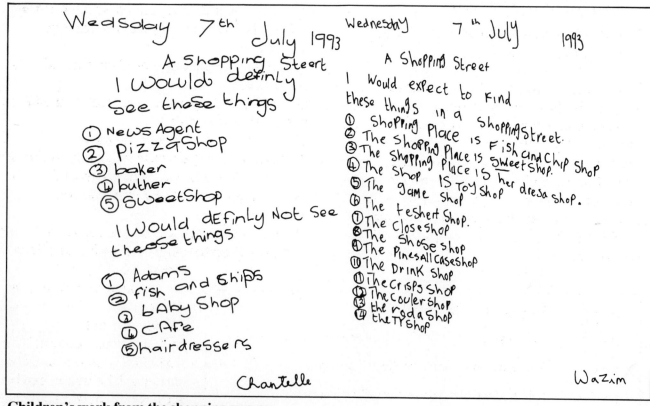

Children's work from the shopping survey.

134

When the children went out to record the shops that were there, they needed to have a tally sheet devised in order to conduct the investigation in an orderly manner. The results were recorded in the form of block graphs or pictograms.

A number of questions arose:
1. Some shops sell more than one thing. Which category should they go into? There is a need for sorting, resorting and classifying.
2. Do building societies and banks actually count as shops?
3. Are there any oddities or surprises?
4. What shops are missing? Can you think of reasons?

The probability scale

At Level 4 of the Number Attainment Target, children are using decimal notation to two decimal places in the context of measurement. This allows them to quantify probability to two decimal places. The probability scale from 0 to 1 gives a measure of the probability of an event. A probability of 0 signifies impossibility, and a probability of 1 signifies certainty. Some examples of this are shown below:

p = 0	Waking up on the moon tomorrow.
p = 0.01	One of your presents next Christmas is worth £200.
p = 0.5	The addition to Sian's family will be a girl.
p = 1	(On Wednesday) Tomorrow will be Thursday.

The probability line can now be labelled with numerical probabilities.

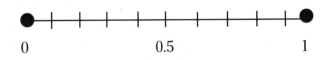

0   0.5   1

It is not always easy to be sure where an outcome should be placed on the probability line, but plenty of experience with the 'washing line', and much practical experimentation will help. Children may not even be aware that the probability of a baby being a girl is very close to 0.5. However, there are some situations for which it is easy to justify an estimate of probability by gathering evidence. Evidence for the probability of a baby being a girl can be gathered by counting the numbers of boys and girls in the class or in the school. The larger amount of evidence gathered from the whole school makes our faith in the estimate stronger.

It is quite difficult to come up with real-life examples of events whose outcome is certain (or impossible) as opposed to being merely very likely (or very unlikely). Advantage can be taken of this by inviting the class to 'pick holes' in suggested examples which purport to do this. The wording is of the utmost importance.

The following exaggerated example shows the problem:
'If I hold Mum's glass vase and let go it will break. That is certain!'
Not if it's only 1 cm above the table.
'If I hold Mum's glass vase *one metre* in the air and let go it will break. That is certain!'
Not if someone catches it or it lands on something soft.
'If I hold Mum's glass vase one metre in the air and drop it on to concrete it will break. That is certain!'
Yes (assuming the concrete has set!)'.

Evidence for the probability of the event 'The next car to come round the corner will be white' can be gathered by making a traffic

survey in which the colours of a large number of cars are noted down. If 7 out of 43 cars are white, an estimate of the probability of the next car being white is 7/43, or about 0.16. Underlying this is the assumption that the sample of cars is representative of all the cars which could come round the corner.

In order to understand the probability scale, children need to understand the decimal number line and the ordering of decimals, and they need to realise the equivalence of the fractional form of a number and its decimal form (for example, that $^1/_4$ equals 0.25). This work does not appear at Level 4 in the Number statements of attainment, but its discussion is essential in connection with the probability scale.

Children can set up an experiment to gather evidence about the probability of success at a fairground game such as throwing a ball into a basket. This event has two possible outcomes:
– the ball will land in the basket (and stay there);
– the ball will not land in the basket.

If 5 throws out of 28 are successful, this gives an experimental probability of 5/28, or 0.18 (to two decimal places). Some questions for exploration are:
– Does the experimental probability change as the ball is thrown more and more times?
– What difference do different conditions make? (We can investigate different distances, the basket at different angles, different balls, and so on.)

– Is there an improvement with practice?
– Are taller people more successful?

Repeating this experiment will help children to become aware that different results may come from the same experiment. Another important idea to be drawn out is that the probability of failure is 1 minus the probability of success.

Children may like to invent other games of chance for the school fête. They should try to set an appropriate charge for the game, to make a reasonable profit.

In the roll-a-penny game shown in Figure 8, the lines are drawn thin and twice as far apart as the width of the coin. The probability of

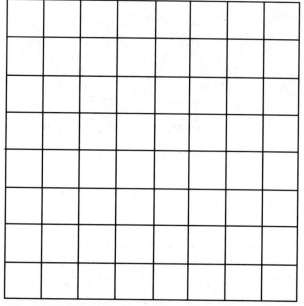

Figure 8: A simple grid for roll-a-penny game.

136

missing the lines in one direction is . The probability of missing the lines in both directions (and so landing entirely inside a square) is $\frac{1}{2} - \frac{1}{2} = 0.25$. It may not be obvious why this is correct – it is valid to multiply the two probabilities because the coin is round (so is the same however it lands) and the two sets of lines are at right-angles (so the result for one direction is independent of that for the other). Try it and see!

It might be useful for the teacher to have the general formula for a square grid in order to calculate the probability for different-sized coins and different line spacing in advance.

The general formula is:

$$\text{Probability of coin landing inside a square} = \frac{(\text{grid width} - \text{coin width})^2}{(\text{grid width})^2}$$

Figure 9 gives an alternative design for a roll-a-penny board: you win if the penny lands

Figure 9: A chequered grid for roll-a-penny.

completely inside a black square, otherwise you lose. The probability is half that for the previous case.

The probabilities should be determined experimentally, of course. (The formula is provided for the teacher's benefit!) The distance between the lines can be adjusted to ensure a healthy profit margin.

Estimating probability

The programme of study uses an imprecise wording which needs clarification.

If the experiment is to look at the *event* 'tossing a die once', then

> Experiment 1 may produce the actual *outcome* '3'
> Experiment 2 may produce the actual *outcome* '4'
> Experiment 3 may produce the actual *outcome* '4'
> and so on.

For each experiment the actual outcome may be different – but they all come from the same set of possible outcomes (1, 2, 3, 4, 5, 6).

'Different outcomes may result' means that the actual result of an experiment can be one of several possible outcomes. Often the *set* of possible outcomes can be very clearly defined (such as rolling a die). However, in less contrived situations it can be difficult or even impossible to classify the set of outcomes without making assumptions.

Example:

Kerry makes a paper dart and the teacher asks the class 'What will happen when Kerry stands under the netball post in the playground and throws the dart towards the opposite post?'

– If distance from the post is all we are interested in, then a well-defined but infinite number of possibilities exist. At the other extreme, we could restrict ourselves to 'under 5m' and '5m or more'.

– We could be interested in the time of flight.

– We might try to consider a much wider range of possibilities:

The dart might be blown away and lost from sight.

It could land on a passing lorry.

It could hit someone in the eye.

A dog might run off with it.

The possibilities are indeed endless, and deciding on the outcomes is subjective. It depends on the interpretation or purpose.

The programme of study uses the questionable wording 'if each of *n* events is assumed to be equally likely' which needs to be interpreted as 'if each of the *n* possible outcomes of an event is assumed to be equally likely'.

Dice and spinners provide material for simple classroom experiments with probability. Children can collect evidence for estimates of probability for the following tasks by repeated experimentation.

1. A game uses a fair, regular twelve-sided spinner giving scores from 1 to 12. If this spinner is not available, is it a fair alternative to throw two dice and add the scores?

2. In some dice games, you have to throw a 6 to start. How many throws do you expect to have before you start?

Children should find that for the first task, the probability of each score on the fair spinner is approximately 0.08. However, when the scores on two dice are added, a score of 1 never occurs, a score of 12 occurs very rarely, and the score with the greatest experimental probability is likely to be 7. Two dice are not a suitable replacement for a fair spinner!

In the above tasks, instead of experimenting to find *experimental probabilities*, it is possible to calculate the *theoretical probabilities*. The possible outcomes when rolling a die are scores of 1, 2, 3, 4, 5, 6. If the

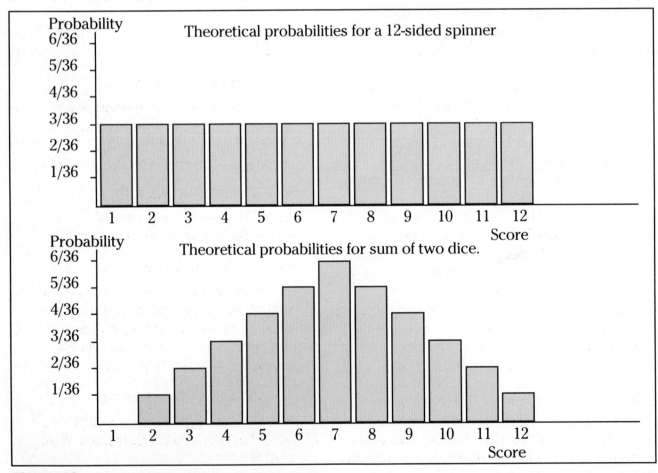

Figure 10

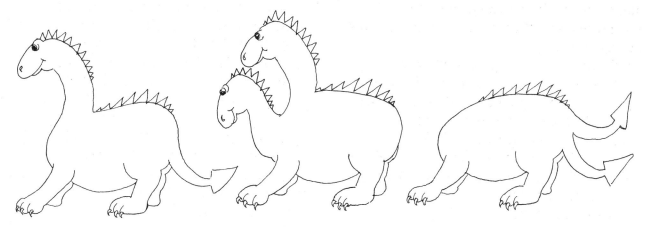

Figure 11

die is fair, all these outcomes are equally likely. (This is an assumption we make.) As there are six possible outcomes, in theory 1/6 of the throws will give a score of 1, 1/6 of the throws will give a score of 2, and so on. The total probability of all the possible outcomes is: 1/6 + 1/6 + 1/6 + 1/6 + 1/6 + 1/6 = 1.

The theoretical probability of a score of 1 = 1/6 = 0.17 (to 2 decimal places).

The theoretical probability of a score of 2 = 1/6 = 0.17 (to two decimal places), etc.

For the two tasks described above, the theoretical probabilities are shown in the graphs in Figure 10. It is quite clear that the two situations are very different.

A very fruitful activity is to allow children to create their own (undoubtedly imperfect) dice and spinners, then experiment with them. The full **PCAI** cycle can occur here: posing questions, collecting the data, analysing, drawing conclusions, then possibly posing more questions and so on.

Children may think that the outcomes of an event are equally likely when they are not. For example, suppose children conduct an imaginary race with three dragons (see Figure 11). One dragon has one head and one tail; the second has two heads and no tail; the third has two tails and no head. At each turn, one dragon moves. Which one moves is determined by tossing two coins. The outcome 'Head, head' means that the dragon with two heads moves, and so on. Children may be surprised that the dragon with one head and one tail is so much more successful than the others. One infant teacher who tried this wrote:

'The reception class really enjoyed this and were quite intrigued by the fact that one dragon always won! It is very useful to do some activities before the level stated in the NC documents; this is one such example.'

If you want to keep your coins safe, seal them in a plastic container with a clear lid. This can also make the tossing easier.

Combining independent events

Level 6

Programme of study

'• identifying all the outcomes when dealing with two combined events which are independent, using diagrammatic, tabular or other forms.'

Statement of attainment

'c) Identify all the outcomes of combining two independent events.'

Programme of study

'• appreciating that the total sum of the probabilities of mutually exclusive events is 1 and that the probability of something happening is 1 minus the probability of it not happening.'

Statement of attainment

'd) Know that the total probability of all the mutually exclusive outcomes of an event is 1.'

two winning tickets out of 100 tickets in the bag. The first person has 2/100 probability of winning (= 0.02 to two decimal places). If the first person wins, then the second person's probability of winning is only 1/99, whereas if the first person loses then the second person's probability of winning is 2/99.

For some purposes, it is convenient to talk about combinations of elementary outcomes, and to describe each combination itself as an outcome. Here is a set of possible elementary outcomes of throwing a die:

Set A

a score of 1

a score of 2

a score of 3

a score of 4

a score of 5

a score of 6

Here is another set of possible outcomes of throwing a die, composed of grouping these outcomes together:

Set B

an even score

an odd score

Outcomes of an event are *mutually exclusive* if they cannot happen at the same time. All the outcomes in Set A are mutually exclusive: if the outcome is a 4, then it cannot at the same time be a 2. Similarly, the two outcomes in Set B are mutually exclusive. However, the outcome 'scoring 6' and the outcome 'scoring an even number' are not mutually exclusive, because 6 is itself an even number and so occurs in both outcomes. A complete set of mutually exclusive outcomes of an event has a total probability of 1, because all the possibilities are included just once. A set of outcomes is said to be *exhaustive* if it covers all possibilities.

Examples illustrating these concepts now follow.

Consider the event of throwing a normal six-sided die and recording the score. The possible scores are: 1, 2, 3, 4, 5, 6.

Two events are *independent* if the outcome of one of them does not affect the probabilities in the other. For example, if a coin is tossed and a die thrown, the face which the coin shows is independent of the score on the die. On the other hand, suppose two people are playing lucky dip, and there are only two winning tickets in the bag. The probability of the second person being successful would depend on the outcome of the first draw: when the first person draws a ticket, that ticket does not go back in the bag. Thus the second person's probability of success is greater if the first person is unsuccessful. For example, suppose there are

1) The two outcomes 'odd' and 'even' are exhaustive. They are also mutually exclusive. They cover all possible scores without duplication (Figure 12).

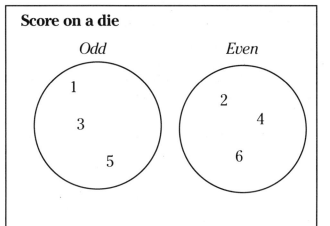

Score on a die

Odd   *Even*

1
3
5

2
4
6

Figure 12
All six scores occur (exhaustive). No score occurs in more than one outcome (mutually exclusive).

2) The two outcomes 'odd', '2' are mutually exclusive but not exhaustive. There are no scores common but some are missing altogether – 4 and 6 (Figure 13).

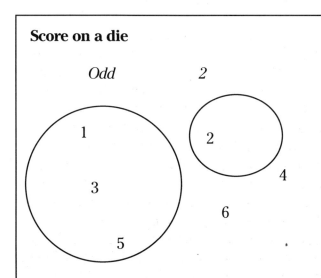

Score on a die

Odd   *2*

1
3
5

2
4
6

Figure 13
Two scores (4 and 6) do not occur in either outcome (so outcomes 'Odd' and '2' are not exhaustive). No score occurs in more than one outcome (so outcomes 'Odd' and '2' are mutually exclusive.

3) The outcomes 'odd', 'not 1' are exhaustive but *not* mutually exclusive. All six possible scores are there, but 3 and 5 occur in both (Figure 14).

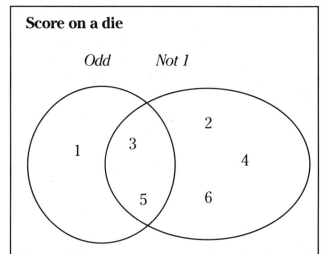

Score on a die

Odd   *Not 1*

1
3
5

2
4
6

Figure 14
All six scores occur (exhaustive). Two scores occur in more than one outcome (not mutually exclusive).

The following task is based on combining the two independent events of throwing a red die and a blue die. The outcomes of the combined event are the scores that result from multiplying the scores on the two dice. The probabilities can be calculated by drawing up a table of all the possible ways the two dice can fall.

A class of 36 children are each allowed to choose a different number, starting with 1 and going up to 36 as determined by their alphabetical position in the register. One child, chosen at random, is to receive a gift. The choice of child is made by throwing a red die and a blue die, and multiplying the scores. Is this fair? The table is shown below.

blue die

X	1	2	3	4	5	6
1	1x1	2x1	3x1	4x1	5x1	6x1
2	1x2	2x2	3x2	4x2	5x2	6x2
3	1x3	2x3	3x3	4x3	5x3	6x3
4	1x4	2x4	3x4	4x4	5x4	6x4
5	1x5	2x5	3x5	4x5	5x5	6x5
6	1x6	2x6	3x6	4x6	5x6	6x6

red die

141

The outcomes are:

blue die

X	1	2	3	4	5	6
1	1	2	3	4	5	6
2	2	4	6	8	10	12
3	3	6	9	12	15	18
4	4	8	12	16	20	24
5	5	10	15	20	25	30
6	6	12	18	24	30	36

(red die labels the left column)

The number of ways in which each possible outcome may occur can now be counted (see Figure 15).

The award of the prize is very unfair. Half the class have no chance of being selected, while the children who choose numbers 6 and 12 have the greatest probability of selection.

Without a systematic approach such a task would be extremely difficult to investigate. By using tables it becomes a relatively easy matter.

National testing

A decade or more ago the Assessment of Performance Unit (APU) conducted national testing of school children and a summarising report prepared at that time by Arthur Owen HMI is reproduced below in edited form. It is as timely today as when he wrote it in 1983. The weaknesses reported may in part have been due to lack of data handling work in primary schools so we can read this and hope for better things to come.

'The APU Primary Survey included practical tests in 'probability' for 11 year olds. In their Report No.2 *Mathematical Development*, the APU give an account of their findings. The Report stated that most curricula included some graphical recording of chance events but the formal theory of probability was not generally considered appropriate for primary school pupils. The APU practical testing on the topic 'probability' was also designed to assess the 11-year-olds' ability to *hypothesise*, to *record* and explain data and to *use data* as a basis for *generalisation* to future events.

Two tests were conducted:
(1) involving an event with two possible outcomes (the tossing of a coin);
(2) involving an event with six outcomes (the rolling of a die).

In each case, pupils were:
(a) asked to predict results that might occur over a specified number of trials;
(b) then asked to test their predictions and record the results;
(c) finally asked to comment on the results obtained and to generalise to future instances.

The pattern of responses was similar in both investigations (coin and die) and can be discussed in terms of ability to *predict*, *record* and *generalise*.

In general, the results showed a disparity between the *quality of predictions* and the *justification* given for them. The vast majority of pupils gave mathematically sound predictions based on the number of alternatives and the number of occurrences. However, when they found that their predictions differed from the experimental results, many pupils reverted to past experience, hunches or cynicism for justification of the results. The more

Outcome	1	2	3	4	5	6	7	8	9	10	11	12
No of ways	1	2	2	3	2	4	0	2	1	2	0	4
Outcome	13	14	15	16	17	18	19	20	21	22	23	24
No of ways	0	0	2	1	0	2	0	2	0	0	0	2
Outcome	25	26	27	28	29	30	31	32	33	34	35	36
No of ways	1	0	0	0	0	2	0	0	0	0	0	1

Figure 15

142

mathematically minded, perhaps more articulate, child was able to live with (or even explain) the discrepancy between theory and practice. These pupils, although rarely using technical terms such as 'random' and 'odds', either referred to 'average results' or, in later discussion, showed that they appreciated the role of chance. Other pupils became confused, either clinging to what they believed must be the mathematically correct answer despite contrary results, or abandoning theory altogether.

To many pupils the test was a new experience, being a situation in which there was no right or wrong answer. Some pupils found it disconcerting to have to justify their beliefs. One tester remarked, "*Why do you think that?* seems an unusual question for most of them and some were quite nonplussed". She added, "Speaking as a teacher .... it's a question we should put a lot more often!'

From *Aspects of Statistics in the Primary and Middle Years*, A. Owen, August 1983.

Arthur Owen's report indicates that there is a clear need for children to *talk* about their probability intuitions, which can help both their mathematical development and their language skills. Indeed, at Key Stages 1 and 2, talking about probability rather than attempting to calculate is the way to proceed.

Activities

Included here is a collection of activities for teachers to adapt for use with their children.

Dragon and treasure

For this Key Stage 1 activity, nine PE hoops are placed in a line on the floor and a child stands in the middle one. In hoop one is a dragon. In hoop nine is gold treasure (see Figure 16).

A die is rolled and if the score is even, the child moves that many hoops towards the dragon. If the score is odd, the child moves that many hoops towards the gold. The game ends with the child finding the gold or being eaten. Before the activity starts there can be much discussion about what is likely to happen – whether the chances are equal, and how many throws it will take to get the gold or be eaten up.

At a higher level, the class can discuss modifications to the game:
– move the starting position to hoop six;
– move three hoops whatever the score;
– if a six is thrown, then throw again;
– if the child correctly predicts odd or even then move that amount towards the gold, otherwise towards the dragon.

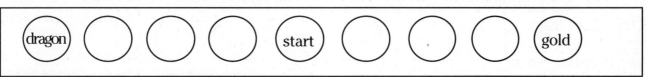

Figure 16

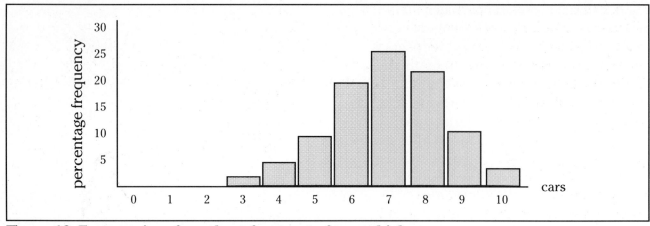

Figure 18: Frequencies of number of cars out of ten vehicles

Vehicle survey and simulation

The purpose of this activity is to investigate whether it is possible to predict the traffic flow on one day, given some factual knowledge about the traffic flowing on a previous occasion.

First you need to do a traffic survey and find out the proportion of cars passing a given point. For example, out of 100 vehicles counted, 70 were cars. This needs to be done on a fairly busy road so that it does not take too long!

Back in the classroom, the teacher asks 'How many cars will there be if we repeat the survey and just ten vehicles are counted?' This can provoke much useful discussion.

Then to test the predictions, without actually repeating the survey, the children are divided into groups of four. A spinner is made for each group by drawing a circle on a sheet of paper and dividing it in the proportions cars: non-cars (70:30 in our case) and using a straightened paper-clip as the pointer (Figure 17).

Figure 17

144

Preparing the spinners might be a good challenge for older children, but in most cases would best be done by the teacher. The circle is drawn on paper, (there is no need to cut it out). The paper-clip pointer is held in place by a pencil (or a drawing pin) and is spun by striking it vigorously at the end.

The children then perform practical simulations using the spinners. In turn, each child completes ten spins and the number of cars is recorded in a tally chart. These results are combined and bar charts drawn. Figure 18 is the theoretical distribution. This shows that seven is the most likely number of cars out of ten vehicles passing, based on the data previously collected (which was 70 out of 100). Note, however, that seven will only occur about a quarter of the time, and six and eight are almost as likely. Note also that there is considerable variation. If 100 such surveys of ten cars are undertaken, then the range of cars can be expected to vary from as low as three (expected once) up to ten (expected three times).

It is clear that the results vary and a single definite right answer cannot be expected. A prediction in terms of a range of answers with some indication of probabilities would be appropriate.

Finally, the class's predictions are put to the test by performing another traffic survey. This should be done one week later than the first survey, at the same time of day. This time groups of ten vehicles are observed and the number of cars noted. This should be repeated until at least ten sets of results are obtained.

Back in the classroom, a final discussion should bring out the uncertainty of knowing exactly what would happen, and the possibility of predicting approximately what would happen, given some factual knowledge and using mathematics and probability simulation.

Registration plates

Introduce this work by asking the children what they know about the numbers and letters on car registration plates. (A visit to the school car park might precede or follow this.)

Stage P – *Pose the question*

Pose the following four questions (using a suitable illustrative example for clarification).
a) Are all digits equally likely?
b) Are all letters of the alphabet equally likely for the single letter?
c) Are all letters of the alphabet equally likely for the letter triplets?
d) Taking only the last letter of the letters triplet, are all letters equally likely?

Stage C – *Collect the data*

To collect the data, either conduct a traffic survey from school as a class, or ask children to bring in data from their neighbourhoods. Ask the children to note vehicle registrations for up to ten vehicles.

F 317 D B C

Note: The single letter (F) signifies the year. The three digits (317) have no particular significance; numbers usually run from 1 to 999. Of the triplet of letters (DBC), normally the last pair (BC) signifies the local authority with whom the vehicle is registered; the first letter (D) does not signify anything in particular. Very old cars have the order reversed, for example DBC 317 F. For more information consult an AA or RAC handbook, or other reference source such as a *Ladybird* or *I-Spy* books.

Stage A – *Analyse the data*

The data are then analysed by constructing tally charts and bar graphs.

Stage I – *Interpret the results*

Having collected and analysed the data in order to answer these questions, the need for some explanation can be pursued. This could be an opportunity for the children to ask at home for suggestions to enrich the class discussion the next day.

The following are suggested as likely findings for the questions posed above:
a) Are all digits equally likely?
No significant difference will be found.
b) Are all letters of the alphabet equally likely for the single letter?
Definitely not. Letters will reflect the frequency of the ages of cars on the road.
Only a few early letters (A,B,C) will be found, but many newer letters (J,K,L ...).
Some letters are not used for signifying year to avoid confusion with digits (for example, I, O).
A humped, asymmetrical distribution will be found if a bar chart is drawn for A,B,C ...M (or whatever the most recent letter is).
c) Are all letters of the alphabet equally likely for the letter triplets?
Definitely not. Some letters will not occur at all. This will vary regionally and locally: S will be very common in or close to Scotland and very rare elsewhere, O will be very common in the

West Midlands, etc.
d) Taking only the last letter of the letters triplet, are all letters equally likely?
Definitely not. The bias reported in c)

Start							Finish

Start							Finish

Figure 19

will be more pronounced because most cars will be locally registered and only a few letters are used locally. Leicester registrations are _UT, _BC, _RY, _NR so common last letters there will be T, C, Y and R.

Eenie, Meenie

Is it fair to use 'Eenie, meenie, minie, mo' to choose who goes first? Is it predictable? What about other choosing strategies?

Car race

A spinner is divided into six equal sectors, which are marked 1,2,1,1,2,1.

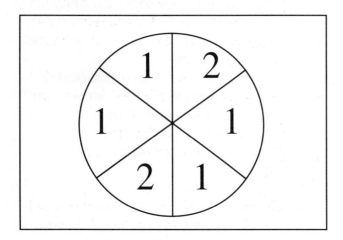

Two children play a car-racing game. The spinner is spun and if 1 comes up, then car 1 moves 1 place along the track. If 2 comes up, then car 2 moves 2 places along the track shown in Figure 19.

Stage P – *Pose the question*

Which is it better to have - car 1 or car 2. Is this a fair game? This situation can evoke heated discussion!

Stage C – *Collect the data*

Play the game.

Stage A – *Analyse results*

A tally chart will be adequate, although for display a bar graph or pie chart might look more interesting.

Stage I – *Interpret results*

Well, is it fair? What about the fact that there are twice as many 1s as 2s?

Guess the coins

The teacher hides five coins in a yoghurt carton and the children have to guess what their total value is.

Clue 1: There are five coins. They are 1p or 5p pieces. What might their total value be? Discussion should lead the class to at least some of the six possibilities.

The teacher displays possibilities on the board, providing help where necessary.

For example:

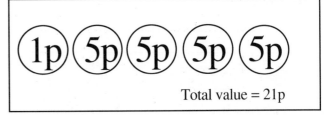

Total value = 21p

Children can choose which combination they think it will be. This will add to their interest.

The class may feel that the two extremes are less likely, since both 1p and 5p coins have been mentioned: 'It is *not likely* to be 5p or 25p.' Many people reading 'There are five coins. They are 1p or 5p pieces' will assume that there must be at least one of each, and ignore the possibility of there being none of one sort. Paying attention to the exact wording is important here (as it often is in mathematical work).

146

Clue 2: There are at least two 5p coins. Which possibilities can be eliminated? Some outcomes which *were* possible *are now* impossible! 'It *might* be 13p or 17p or 21p or 25p.' 'It *cannot* be 5p or 9p.'

Clue 3: There are more 1p coins than 5p coins. This leads to *certainty* of the contents of the yoghurt carton: 'It *must* be 13p!'

A nice way to end this activity is to construct a table:

No of 1p coins:	5	4	3	2	1	0
No of 5p coins:	0	1	2	3	4	5
Total value (p):	5	9	13	17	21	25

This works well on a spreadsheet.

Spinners – same or different?

Comparing spinners such as the four below can be a valuable activity at a variety of levels, involving all four stages of the **PCAI** cycle. In each case the question is 'Which number will come up more often, or will they come up about equally?'. Young children very often count the number of sectors and ignore the areas (or angles). Predictions can be very wrong and resolving the conflict between prior belief and experimental results is a valuable exercise.

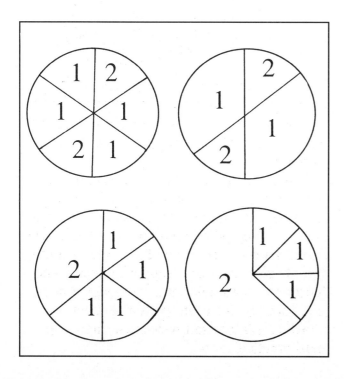

Fruit machines

Make a hexagonal spinner as below and use it to simulate a simple fruit machine. (You could use a paper-clip as a pointer).

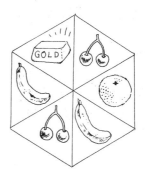

Game 1

Children each choose a different symbol.
Then the rules are explained.
The winner is to get one counter.
– If we play just once, who is going to win? Are we sure? Why?
– If we play lots of times, who is going to win most? Are we sure? Why?
 Play the game once and see what happens.
– Who won the counter? Who guessed right?
– Who is going to win next time? Are we sure?
 Play the game again.
– Who won the counter? Who guessed right?
– Who is going to win next time? Are we sure?
 Play the game again, and so on.
– Who won most counters? Why?
– Was that what we said would happen?

Game 2

The children each choose a different symbol. Then the rules are explained. If GOLD comes up, the winner gets four counters. The other symbols win three counters.
– Which symbol is best?
– Which is worst?
– If we play just once, who is going to win? Are we sure? Why?
– If we play lots of times, who is going to win most? Are we sure? Why?
 Play the game once and see what happens.
– Who won the counter? Who guessed right?
– Who is going to win next time? Are we sure?
 Play the game again.
– Who won the counter? Who guessed right?
– Who is going to win next time? Are we sure?

Play the game again, and so on.
– Who won most counters? Why?
– Was that what we said would happen?

Game 3

Repeat Game 2 with the rule that GOLD is rewarded with five counters.

Game 4

Make a second hexagonal spinner as below.

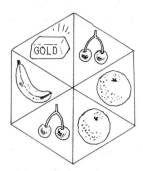

How will this one be different? Say what you think will happen. Then do experiments. Compare its performance with the first spinner.

Games 5 to 7

Repeat games 1 to 3, using the second spinner.

Game 8

Use both hexagonal spinners together.
– Which pair is easiest to get? Is it a *BANANA* and an *ORANGE*?
– Which pair is hardest? Is it *CHERRIES* and *GOLD*?
   Each child chooses a combination such as '*GOLD* and *ORANGE*' from the list:

GOLD	–	GOLD
CHERRIES	–	CHERRIES
ORANGE	–	ORANGE
BANANA	–	BANANA
GOLD	–	BANANA
GOLD	–	ORANGE
GOLD	–	CHERRIES
BANANA	–	ORANGE
BANANA	–	CHERRIES
ORANGE	–	CHERRIES

The order of the two symbols is not important. The two spinners are spun, and the winner gets a counter.
   Who is going to win?
   Play the game many times, and record the results in a chart like the one below.

second spinner

	banana	orange	gold	cherries
banana				
orange				
gold				
cherries				

first spinner

– Who won most counters? Why?
– Was that what we said would happen?

Game 9

Each child is given ten counters. Each child then chooses a different combination from the list below. It is important that the first two are chosen, the rest are less important.

GOLD	–	GOLD
CHERRIES	–	CHERRIES
ORANGE	–	ORANGE
BANANA	–	BANANA
GOLD	–	BANANA
GOLD	–	ORANGE
GOLD	–	CHERRIES
BANANA	–	ORANGE
BANANA	–	CHERRIES
ORANGE	–	CHERRIES

Then the rules are explained. *GOLD – GOLD* wins three counters. All the others win just one counter.
– Is it fair?
– Who will win the most money?
– Who will win no money?
   Play the game many times and see.

148

Game 10

Divide the children into two teams. Each team has five counters.

One team is the *CHERRIES* team. The other team is the *NOT CHERRIES* team. In turn each team spins the spinner.

If *CHERRIES – CHERRIES* is spun, the *CHERRIES* team wins one counter from the *NOT CHERRIES* team. Otherwise the *CHERRIES* team pay one counter to the other team.

Is this fair? Who will have more money at the end?

Play it and see...

Game 11

Divide the children into two teams. Each team has five counters.

One team is the *CHERRIES* team. The other team is the *NOT CHERRIES* team. In turn each team spins the spinner.

If *CHERRIES* comes up on either or both spinners, the *CHERRIES* team wins one counter from the *NOT CHERRIES* team. Otherwise the *CHERRIES* team pay one counter to the *NOT CHERRIES* team.

Is it fair? Who will have more money at the end?

Play it and see...

DIME probability kits

These useful kits are described in Chapter 2 and can form the basis of many investigations at the upper end of Key Stage 2.

Home-made spinners and dice

Children should be encouraged to make their own spinners and dice – this raises important questions about fairness, bias and the need for symmetry. What happens if the die is a cuboid and not a cube? What happens if the spinner's angles are not equal?

Dolly Mixtures and Smarties activities

The notes on the following pages give outline ideas for Key Stage 1 activities involving sorting, recording and probability. The apparatus required is: some packets of Dolly Mixtures and some of the mini-packets of Smarties. The Dolly Mixtures recording sheet overleaf, shows the shapes and their associated names, and the Smarties recording sheet may be helpful.

Dolly Mixtures

Predicting

What will be inside the packet?
(Sweets – Dolly Mixtures – number – shapes – colours – flavours)

Each group member records his or her own predictions.

Checking

Open the packet. Were you right? Exactly? Nearly? How wrong?

Who predicted best? Are there some surprises?

Sorting

Sort the sweets (no way specified). Now do it another way (shapes, colours, tastes, favourites ...).

Mind-reading

Put all the sweets back together. One person decides on a criterion to sort into two or more categories, and begins to sort in front of the group. The others try to guess what that criterion is. Then someone else has a go.

Recording

Record contents of the packet by *shape* on a graph.

How many shapes are there? What shall we call them (cube, tube, dube, jelly)? (See the Dolly Mixtures recording sheet.)

Record, using:
– Objects themselves
– Pictograms – one picture representing one sweet/one picture representing several sweets
– Tallying – simple strokes
　　　　 – five-bar gate system
　　　　 – own invented method
(Words or pictures may be used to illustrate the shapes)

Sorting

Ask everyone in the group to choose a shape *and* to choose a colour.

Using the sweets themselves and a Carroll diagram, sort with the two chosen criteria into four groups.

For example, suppose the choice is JELLY and RED, then sort by JELLY/OTHERS and RED/NOT RED:

	red	not red
jellies		
others		

– Are there more jellies or more red jellies?
– How many are jellies?
– How many are *not* jellies?
– Who in the group will get the most?
– What two criteria give the largest set of sweets?
– What two criteria give the smallest set of sweets?
– Are the two criteria independent? How can we tell?

Recording

Enter each group member's name on the special Dolly Mixtures recording sheet showing all the shapes.

Use a mapping diagram to record for each group member their first favourite shape (*red* line) and second favourite shape (*green* line).

Predicting

Pupils take turns to take a Dolly Mixture of the pupil's first choice shape from the packet. When the first choice is all gone, the second choice may be taken. A child drops out when both chosen shapes are no longer available. Taking a sweet continues until no pupil is able to take one.

Will any shapes not be taken at all? How many will be left? Who will get most?

Lucky dip 1

Choose one kind, for example tube-shaped sweets (which we call *tubes*), and create a graph showing the frequencies of the colours. Check it against the actual sweets.

Put all the *tubes* into an opaque bag.

If each child picks a *tube* without looking, what colour will he or she pick?

Each child *keeps* on the table the sweet picked. Then the next child picks.

Record the results of the experiment by building up a new graph, basically the same as the first graph.

Continue until all *tubes* are taken.

Compare the results graph with the original graph. Are they the same? Why? Why not?

Lucky dip 2

Check the frequency graph against the actual *tube* sweets, until all are satisfied it is correct. Count the *tubes*.

Put all the *tubes* into an opaque bag. If each child picks a *tube* without looking, what colour will he or she pick? Do this, with the chooser trying to predict each time. Record if the prediction is correct or wrong each time (optional).

Each child *replaces* the sweet in the bag. Then the next child picks. Record the results of the experiment by building up a new graph basically the same as the first graph.

Continue taking turns until the number of sweets taken (and replaced) equals the number of sweets being used.

Compare the results graph with the original frequency graph. Are they the same? Why? Why not?

Detectives 1

The teacher prepares a bag secretly containing just two different sorts of *dube* Dolly Mixtures (for instance orange/white and green/white). Firstly the proportions are equal.

Children take turns to select a *dube*, record it, then replace it. At each stage the group tries to predict the contents of the bag. They continue until they are confident they know

150

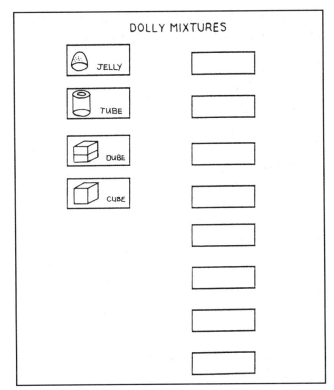

Dolly Mixtures recording sheet.

the proportions then open the bag to check. This is repeated with unequal proportions.

Detectives 2

The teacher prepares a bag secretly containing just two different sorts of *dube* Dolly Mixtures (for example, brown/white and pink/white). The proportions are to be equal, three or four of each.

Children take turns to select two *dubes*, record the pair, then replace them. At each stage the group tries to predict the contents of the bag. They continue until they are confident. Then they open the bag and check.

Do some pairs (for example, both brown) occur more often than other pairs (for example, both pink, or one of each)? Is there an explanation? Does it make any difference if there are more (or less) sweets used?

Smartie packets

It is better to use small packets rather than tubes, as they are cheaper, contain a more manageable quantity for infants, and have a greater variety between packets.

Share out the packets between groups. Give each group one packet, and tell them not to open it yet.

Predicting

Own group's packet
What will be inside your packet (sweets – smarties – number – colours)?

Each group member records its own packet predictions (a simple frequency table, perhaps).

Other group's packet
What will be in other people's packets? Will they all be the same? (number – colour)

Record the prediction simply as 'same' or 'different'.

Checking

Own group's packet
Open your own packet. Were you right? Exactly? Nearly? How wrong? Who predicted best?

Recording

Record contents of your own packet by colour. How many colours are there? Do we all agree?

Record, using:
– objects;

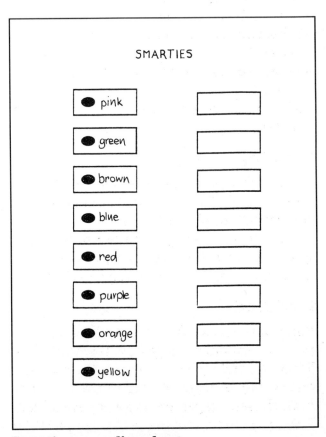

Smarties recording sheet.

– pictograms;
– tallying – five bar gate;

Comparing

Other group's packet
Make a note of own results, and exchange graph of results with other group.
– Is their packet the same as ours?
– Do they have the same number? Is it fair?
– Do they have the same colours? The same names for colours? Does it matter? (Is it fair?)

Checking

Exchange packets. Did they record the information correctly? Compare the packet with the graph.

Recording.

Record comparison of own and other group's packets (double sided bar graph perhaps).

Sorting

Retrieve own packet and graph.
  Sort the Smarties (no way specified).
  Now do it another way (colours, tastes, favourite/non-favourite, light/dark).

Recording

Ask everyone in the group to state their favourite colour (or simply to choose a colour). Record using mapping.

Predicting

Turns are taken to take a Smartie of the pupil's chosen colour from the packet. A child drops out when the chosen colour is no longer available. Taking the Smarties is to continue until no pupil is able to take one because all the chosen colours are gone.
– Will any colours not be taken?
– How many Smarties will be left?
– Who will get most?
  Record the results for each pupil. Infants will need to do this physically. Juniors may be able to predict without using the 'apparatus'.

Checking

Exchange results and packet with another group and check their predictions.

Gamesmanship

Start afresh. Is it better to forego one's favourite/chosen colour in order to secure more Smarties? Does it matter how the choosing is done?

Extension

Suppose a second choice is allowed?

Whole Class

What are the ranges of numbers of different colours? How can this be displayed?

Reasoning

Why are the packets all the same/different?
  Assuming there is some difference:
– Could they be made to be all the same?
– Could your group and the next group work together so that both packets are the same?
– Would it be better if all packets were the same?

Further reading

Mathematical Activities from Poland
Cwirko - Godycki, J. (ATM, 1979).
What Are My Chances? Books A and B
A.P. Shulte and S.A. Choate (Creative Publications, 1977).
* *Get It Together* Erickson, T (*Equals* series, University of California,1989). Pages 8 – 15, 100 – 111 provide an unusual way of doing probability activities which stimulates much discussion rich in mathematical language.
Probability Games (Ladbroke Mathematics Team, Royal Borough of Kensington and Chelsea).

* Available from Jonathan Press in the UK.

Chapter Nine
Cross-curricular issues and data handling

Spoken language

Spoken language has been seen increasingly as important in the development of mathematical thinking. Language is the child's means of developing understanding, by saying thoughts out loud, questioning, predicting and so on. This fact is reflected in Attainment Target 1– Using and Applying Mathematics at Key Stage 1, which might be translated as:

Level 1   I can talk about what I've done and ask questions.
              I can guess what happens next.
Level 2   I can talk about my work and check the results.
              I can change the question and say what will happen if I do and why.
Level 3   I can talk/ask questions about what I have done using mathematical language.

It is important that teachers try to develop pupils' mathematical terminology. Learning about probability at Key Stage 1, for example, is very much an attempt to attach words and meanings to concepts which may be personal and quite difficult to define.

Vocabulary such as 'chance', 'possible', 'unlikely', 'very likely' and so on are individual impressions based on personal experiences. For the Key Stage 1 teacher it is the discussion of graphs, tally sheets and pictorial representations that is the key component of the data handling strand of the mathematics curriculum. This is why large-scale and flexible methods of displaying data are important.

Children should be encouraged to ask questions, and to question the meaning and validity of data from the outset. The discussion has to be structured and should not be allowed to develop into chatter. One method which has been used successfully is to have a five-minute recall at the end of a session, where children are encouraged to present their ideas. They quickly become comfortable with this approach and use it to tease out ideas and explanations.

Data handling – let the children move

Data handling can be introduced outside the four walls of the classroom. In a more informal environment children can 'act out' data handling activities, and this will encourage the development of social skills at the same time. Below are two examples of this.

Sorting children – get in line

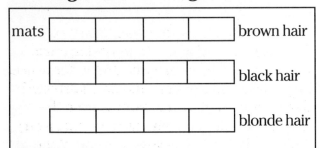

Figure 1

Children stand on the appropriate mat, according to their hair colour, for example, children with brown hair go to this mat.
– How many to a mat?
– Hold hands... which is the longest line?
Change the criterion, for example, children with blue eyes, brown eyes.
– How many? What if? Which?
The above sorting and categorising activity, which embraces language work, could be enacted using hoops instead of mats.

Figure 2

The link with graphical representation is clear. The total length of hoops, mats or children holding hands represents, in an approximate fashion, the number of children with hair of a given colour. A line or bar graph would do this more accurately.

Branching – follow the pathway

Paths are drawn in the playground (or in the hall perhaps) using chalk, and pupils have to walk along the paths, taking decisions at the junctions. One example is shown in Figure 3.

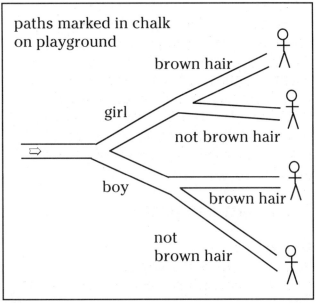

Figure 3

This can be extended with a large number of possible destinations. Children should be encouraged to describe their journey along the pathways, and give reasons for the route they took.

Cross-curricular topics

It is not always easy to incorporate meaningful data-handling situations into a cross-curricular theme. There are obstacles which tend to get in the way. Firstly, in instances where a commercial scheme is followed rigidly, teachers may be reluctant to depart from it or may be discouraged from doing so. Secondly, when the teacher decides upon a theme it needs to be fairly broad to encompass the varying requirements of the National Curriculum subjects. It should also, however, enable the teacher to focus on particular areas of work without too much artificiality. If a year's work is planned for a

Year 2 class, for example, it might look something like this:

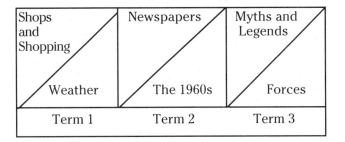

Shops and Shopping / Weather	Newspapers / The 1960s	Myths and Legends / Forces
Term 1	Term 2	Term 3

The main focus might be on history (as in The 1960s/Myths and legends), geography (as in Newspapers/Shops and shopping/Weather) or science (as in Forces) and this might lead the teacher to concentrate on attainment targets and programmes of study for those subjects. If we take the example of Myths and legends (see the topic web in Figure 4) a broader approach might be possible:

Myths and legends

History
What is a myth and a legend?
Legends from history, such as Greek, Norse, British
Legends as stories
How are they passed down?
Can any of them be true?
AT 1, AT 2

English
Story telling and listening
Legends in poetry
Story writing
Other cultures and legends
Drama – acting out legends
AT 1, AT 2, AT 3

Technology
Generating ideas for a puppet theatre
Planning and making a puppet theatre
Writing scripts, making scenery, costumes
Working in groups
Giving a performance
AT 1, AT 2, AT 3, AT 4

Different teachers in different circumstances may place these in a different order of priority. For one class history may be the main focus but for another class it might be technology, and for another English and so on.

Having established the main thrust of the topic, elements of music (composing music to accompany the puppet theatre performance, music based on legends) and art (illustrated manuscripts, mythical creatures from the past in churches and illustrations and so on) could be drawn in. Towards the end of the planning process it may become apparent that there is limited scope for science and mathematics (perhaps some measurement through technology). What opportunities

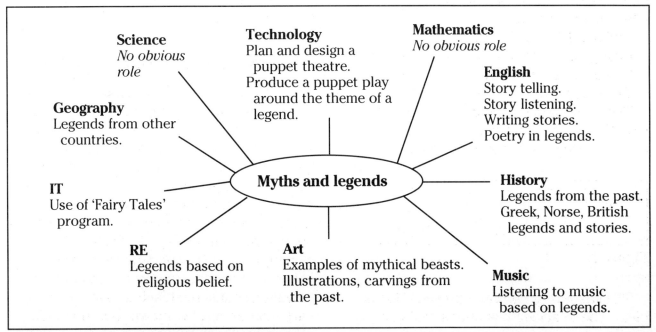

Figure 4: A topic web for Myths and legends.

present themselves for data handling? The answer would appear to be very few indeed! Points to note are:

• It is not always possible to incorporate data handling activities into a cross-curricular theme. This should not worry the teacher, as opportunities will arise elsewhere. To force data handling artificially is unwise and counter-productive, undermining the emphasis on *purposeful* data handling.

• Any data handling investigation needs to begin with a problem, a question posed which actually excites the children, i.e. an open-ended question which may well have a range of possible answers. If no question can be formulated then the teacher will have to consider other ways to introduce the subject. There is a danger of continuing activities which become meaningless to the children.

• Very few themes are selected purely on the basis of the mathematical activities which can be drawn into them; the teacher's primary objectives may lie in history, geography and science. Despite this, there will often be latent opportunities for data handling work which can be developed provided the teacher takes the time to think about the situation and asks some appropriate initial questions.

• The National Curriculum does not explicitly encourage cross-curricular work. The layout and requirements of the documents are varied and in some instances seem contradictory. Unless the teacher is experienced enough to know each subject area well, opportunities may be missed. This is certainly the case with Key Stage 2; it is easier and more traditional to work in a cross-curricular way within Key Stage 1.

• Finally, as has been shown previously, there are real opportunities to present the children with statistical investigations from all areas of the curriculum which are real, meaningful, purposeful and exciting. There is a role here for the mathematics co-ordinator, in supporting staff and making suggestions to ensure that opportunities for purposeful data handling are not missed. There is a strong case for the co-ordinator to initiate school-based INSET and raise awareness of the possibilities of using data handling in cross-curricular work.

Support, ideas and suggestions need to be given sensitively, remembering that many teachers feel under pressure and are not mathematics specialists. It might even be argued that for Key Stages 1 and 2 the data handling activities contained in any commercial scheme being used should be disregarded and attention drawn to the possibilities of incorporating data handling only through topic work. This suggestion would certainly open up debate within the staffroom, which is no bad thing if the idea is to raise awareness about how data handling should be taught!

Shops and shopping

The list of curriculum areas where data handling may arise also includes technology (designing posters) and English (role-play). Taking, for example, the theme of Shops and shopping, the data handling component could be based on questions the children are likely to pose – perhaps as a result of class discussion.
– What shops do we have in our street?
– How can we sort them?
– How can they be grouped?
– How do the shops differ?
– What shops *should* we have?
– How can we record this information?

Attainment targets	
	Geography
AT 1	Talking about places I know
	Land use
	Mapping skills
	Following routes
AT 2	Talking about features in the environment
AT 4	Talking about settlements/goods/services provided
AT 5	Improving the local environment
	Mathematics
AT 1	Use of money
AT 2	Shopping problems
AT 3	Routes and location
	Shopping surveys
	(e.g. Which shops would we like to have?)
	History
	Shops in the past
AT 1	Development of shops
AT 3	Shops then/now (e.g. goods, organisation, advertising)
	RE
	Shops in other countries
	Markets/goods/trade
	Art
AT 1	Observing the local environment
	Drawing, painting, collage work
	Designing displays for shop windows

– What shops do local people feel they need?
– How can we find out?
– Who should see this information? Why?
It has to be emphasised that data handling is more than number manipulation or artistic presentation. Data handling is usually about people, their feelings, preferences and in some cases their life histories. The earlier that children understand this, the more approachable the subject will be.

When statistical investigations are conducted through the medium of cross-curricular themes the children can become involved and can empathise with the people under investigation, whether this be clients at a tuck shop or the citizens of London during the Plague. There is a social dimension to children collecting data. Surveys are difficult to conduct in isolation; they require the child to cooperate, compromise, argue a case and persist with an investigation – all social skills which schools want to encourage. Children also need to present their findings, make suggestions, reflect and approach situations with an open mind. This may well be considered the province of the English curriculum, but should be at the heart of any statistical investigation.

Differentiation

Most primary teachers have a class of mixed ability children. The spread of ability, even with very young children, can be quite wide. Approaching data handling through cross-curricular themes allows children to work at their own level. For example, during a topic on minibeasts children had to investigate the appearance of minibeasts in different locations around the school site (under a log or stone, in a grass verge or bush and so on).

This information needed to be recorded and presented to the rest of the class. Some of the children were only ready to record that information diagrammatically, as in Figure 5.

Figure 5

When this record was explained to the other children, the teacher asked questions aimed at developing the individual's ability to put thoughts into words, to predict, to explain and so on:
– Which minibeast was most common?
– How did you manage to count each minibeast?
– Did you ever run out of squares to record in? What did you do?
– What would you do next time?

Although this form of representation worked for a stone, it became unmanageable for a log as far too many minibeasts were found and iconic representation (on a one-to-one basis) was impractical. The simpler tally chart method was adopted thereafter. Other children within the class recorded this information for themselves in block graphs or bar graphs.

It was useful to make recordings at different times of the day and under different weather conditions, and to display this information and draw conclusions from it. In this way children were not only working at their own level but also contributing to the 'whole' – adding a piece to the jigsaw, discussing with and questioning each other.

The thematic approach allows for an understanding of the need to produce more accurate and sensitive information sheets in a way that a commercial scheme could not. It also gives the teacher the freedom to lead, intervene, develop and suggest. The teacher knows the children and their potential, and can use this knowledge to pursue a line of investigation.

Children, statistics and health

Children become spellbound when talking about the Plague, the Black Death or conditions of life in Victorian England. There are numerous ways in which data can be collected and used creatively (and obviously sensitively) about health and hygiene, as the following example illustrates.

During a history topic on Tudors and Stuarts (a core study unit) children were exposed to simplified extracts from Defoe's *Journal of a Plague Year* which gives statistics for the spread of the plague month by month, parish by parish. These data were recorded, patterns sought and the reasons for the patterns considered, incidentally giving children the chance to operate with relatively large numbers. Placed in the context of real human stories of suffering, ignorance and fears the data handling work was a thought-provoking experience.

In a later lesson children listed the advertisements to be found in the pages of a Victorian newspaper, many of which were for patented cures and medicines claiming to cure all manner of ills. When recorded and compared to a modern-day newspaper, startling differences were revealed. The teacher then asked for an explanation of the differences in these two sets of data and a lively discussion followed.

'The Victorians' is also a core study unit for Key Stage 2 History. The above examples may seem gruesome but they certainly show the human face of statistics, something that should not be overlooked.

The incidental opportunities of school life

A teacher reports on what children remember of their school work:

'I once conducted an informal survey at the end of a school year with a class of Year 4 children. I asked them to describe something 'remarkable' that had happened at school. I suppose I wanted some feedback on lessons I had taken which I hoped were memorable. Did my choice of 'remarkable experiences' coincide with theirs? No!

'Not one child mentioned a lesson. Instead, they came up with: Sports day, Christmas productions, assemblies... Teachers can sometimes marginalise such 'extra curricular' activities, they can even become something of a chore, but my survey shows that the children have a different perspective and such activities and experiences can be very important to them.'

At a time when the demands on time become ever greater, it can be difficult to justify the effort required to produce a class assembly, or to organise a sports day or some other special event. These activities can be turned to advantage. They are real situations and the results of statistical investigations can have real impact on the children's life in school, thereby showing the relevance of data handling. Three different situations (there are many more) now follow, which give an idea of what can be done.

First, a West Midlands teacher reports on a local topic, then two more general examples are briefly outlined.

Carnival

'We are in a multicultural environment, and have children from many different ethnic backgrounds. In June of every year we organise a carnival which involves costumes, music, food, drink, stalls, entertainments, parades and so on. There are opportunities for children to conduct surveys to ascertain which type of music should be played, which types of stall/entertainment are most successful (bearing in mind that the needs of children from ages 3-11 must be catered for). Information gathered in this way can be stored on a database and used to plan the next carnival. At the end of the carnival there may be opportunities to evaluate, perhaps gather different information, or interpret the information in a different way.'

Sports day

Are records kept? What are the differences in times between the different age groups for running, skipping, long jump? Is there a link between size and achievement? Are times improving? Can children be matched to the most suitable event according to physique? Does practice/training make a difference to achievement?

There are many opportunities to include a sports day investigation within the curriculum. Comparing one year's results with the next can be part of producing school records. The role of the computer can be central to this kind of investigation for storing and analysing data year by year. Children can store details of their own achievements and have them updated on a regular basis.

Class assembly – The First World War (Remembrance Day)

Read extracts from some of Lyn MacDonald's work, talk about poppies, show slides of conditions in the trenches and then introduce the statistics. For example, you (the soldier in the trench) had a 1 in 5 chance of being killed and a 2 in 5 chance of being wounded.

It is important in this kind of work to link people to the numbers. By using children as the soldiers and drawing cards, rolling dice or twisting spinners to provide the instances of wounding and death, a powerfully revealing simulation can ensue. Which members of the class survive unharmed? How many out of the class are killed? Then one can begin to consider more general questions by drawing inferences from the data provided and from the simulation results. Would some families have lost more than one person? What was the chance of an individual surviving unharmed?

Data handling and technology

Technology is a relatively new subject to many primary teachers. It involves perceiving needs and opportunities (Attainment Target 1), generating a design (Attainment Target 2), planning and making (Attainment Target 3) and evaluation (Attainment Target 4).

One crucial element of a design technology project is that of research; this research may well be based on some form of statistical investigation. A specific example will be given briefly, later. If some of the requirements of the National Curriculum Technology document are listed, it is easy to see that they have many characteristics also to be found within data handling situations:

Finding out
Asking questions to make decisions
Talking about ideas
Gathering information in different ways
Explaining things
Deciding upon sources of information
Telling people about my work
Using information to develop ideas
Changing ideas because of what I found out

Example – Reading book project

A class of Year 6 children was divided into groups and presented with the task of producing a reading book (one per group) for a group of Year 2 children. Time was limited, which meant work had to be shared out and then brought back together. Figure 6 shows some questions and thoughts which arose in planning and carrying out the work.

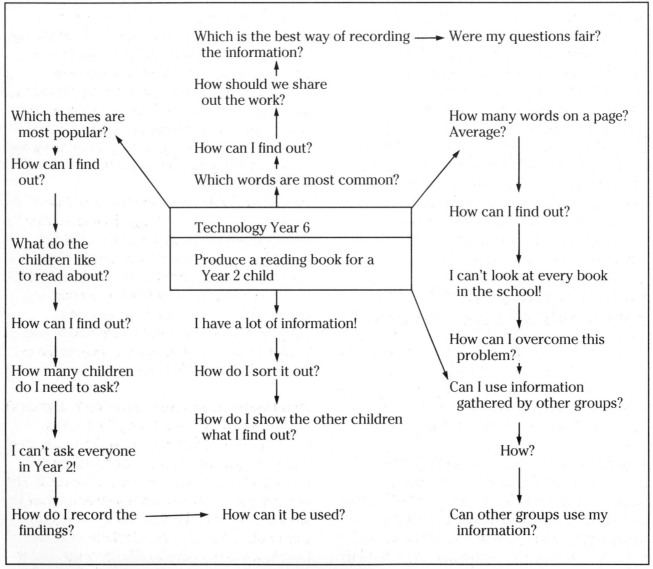

Figure 6: Draft ideas diagram for reading book project.

P	C	A	I
Possible questions	What information do I need? How shall I record it?	How shall I represent the data?	What conclusions can I draw?
Q1 How many words on a page?			
Q2			
etc.			

Figure 7

It would be useful to reinterpret the information in terms of the **PCAI** cycle and possibly put it into tabular form (Figure 7).

Data had to be collected concerning the number of words used on a page and the most common words. This information had to be gathered, recorded and made understandable to others in the group who did not have a hand in its collection. Children also needed to decide how to use this information. Surveys and questionnaires had to be designed, implemented and interpreted in order to find out the most popular themes or types of story Year 2 children liked to read. The Year 6 children were surprised with what they found. For them this was the first time they had experienced the value of collecting data; they came to realise that one's own pre-conceived assumptions about a subject may be incompatible with the facts.

Using *Practical Guides* for data handling opportunities

Data handling is not restricted to mathematics lessons and can arise naturally from other areas of the school curriculum. The following *Practical Guides* books (Scholastic Publications) may provide further ideas.

Practical Guides Mathematics (Andy Bailey, Lynda Townsend and Mike Wilkinson)
Each chapter provides a variety of both open-ended and structured activities and there are many suggestions for building cross-curricular links. The open-ended activities, in particular, offer many opportunities for purposeful data handling. For example, the activity 'Past Times' looks at how children can tap into a direct link with the past through their parents and grandparents.

Practical Guides Technology (Douglas P. Newton and Lynn B. Newton)
Data handling has two key aspects within technology. Firstly, children will be designing, planning, making and evaluating an artefact, system or environment which involves measurement and data processing. Secondly, they will engage with information technology – using calculators, computer databases and spreadsheets, requiring storing, processing and presenting information by electronic means.

Practical Guides Science (Graeme Kent)
Topics covered at Key Stage 1 include Myself, Families, Senses, School, Homes, Holidays, Toys, Shapes, Forces, Water, Travel, Weather and Hot and cold and the author discusses the contributions to each from Science, Design and Technology, Mathematics, Geography, History, Art, English and Music. Topics covered at Key Stage 2 include Trees, Clothes, Bells and Torches.

Practical Guides Geography (Rachel Bowles)
An extract concerning 'Using the locality' is reproduced in Figure 8 overleaf. A few minutes' thought about any of the entries will reveal the potential for data handling. Chapter 2 'The enquiry approach' presents a structure very similar to the **PCAI** model used throughout this book. Other chapters include work on health, weather, maps and land usage. Using IT is thoroughly covered in Chapter 6.

Level	AT1	AT2	AT3	AT4	AT5
1	Walk round school. Find school on a map. Make a model of some part of the school.	Describe what has been seen. What important building is there? What is its name?	Which way does the pavement or playground slope? Are we on a hill or in a valley?	Who else lives or works in the street or school? How do they travel home/ to work?	What is good about the street or playground? What spoils it?
2	Find a street or area near school and observe in groups the details of contrasting buildings.	Talk about the contrasts. Look at old photographs and relate them to the present. When did changes happen? Where else are such buildings found in the locality?	Where are the wet and dry places? Why? Where are hills and valleys? How far away are they?	Where do people come from to this place? Where do they go to buy books? Food? How do they get there?	Where do the bricks come from? What could make the street/park better?
3	Make a map showing the route home from school in the correct sequence. Select a place on the map for investigating.	Visit several places in the locality and use maps, photographs and archive material to find out more about them. How differentare they from each other?	Discover why the places are different in location (e.g. streams, lakes ponds). Where is the highest hill?	Find out why the land is used differently (e.g. Why are allotments here and not there?) Why is it more difficult to reach some places than others?	Investigate a brick-field. Think of some solutions to unsightly areas in the locality. What causes 'dumps'?
4	Use measuring equipment in the playground and the locality (e.g. as part of planning a garden).	Find out why certain buildings (e.g. library), land uses (e.g. park) and activities such as shopping are located at particular sites.	Investigate where the local streams start and finish. Measure changes in the stream during the year. When Is the water level highest? Lowest?	Compare the advantages and disadvantages of the different means of transport in the area. Why is one quicker than the other?	Find out where the local water supply comes from. How is the water supplied?
5	Obtain information from the 1:25 000 and 1:50 000 OS maps.	Investigate the major influences in the home region and fit the locality into the region. What is it like? Where do we fit?	Investigate good local examples of weathering and erosion and relate to changes in the locality (e.g. churchyard and stream). How long does a name last on a tomb stone?	Find out why the population size has changed over the region. Where are the new houses? Where are the empty houses?	Chart the possible causes of pollution of the local water and suggest remedies. Where does the polluted area start?

Figure 8: Using the locality – some aspects.

162

Chapter 10
Resources

Finding appropriate resource material for data handling is not always easy. New materials are being produced all the time, so it is difficult to keep up to date. Addresses for products discussed in this chapter are given at the end of the chapter.

Sources of secondary data

• Newspapers – both local and national – are excellent sources of secondary data (that is, compiled by others). The teacher might like to skim through papers and cut out potentially useful tables or other items, and build up a file for future use.

• The ten-yearly national Census of Population reports available at local libraries (last one 1991) aim to count all the people in the UK and to find out about their home, occupation, education, car ownership and other things. The government also uses the less expensive and quicker sample surveys which select representative people or businesses to find out all kinds of information,

such as what people spend their money on. The type of survey most often reported in the media is opinion polls. Subjects covered vary greatly – religion, consumer products, politics, attitudes to crime and so on. Private industry also conducts opinion polls to determine the market and consumer demand for their current or future products. The Consumers' Association provides detailed reports in its *Which?* series of magazines on a wide range of products and services.

• *Social Trends* is an annual government publication prepared by the Central Statistical Office (CSO) and published by HMSO, covering such categories as: Population, Households and Families, Leisure and Transport. It presents data under the following categories:
– Population
– Households and families
– Education
– Employment
– Income and wealth
– Expenditure and resources

– Health and personal social services
– Housing
– Environment
– Leisure
– Participation
– Law enforcement
– Transport.

Comparisons over time and with other countries are included.

Sources used in gathering the data for *Social Trends* include among others the following government surveys:
– The Family Expenditure Survey
– The Survey of Retail Prices
– The General Household Survey
– The Census of Population

Primary text books

Historically, statistics has not been considered an important part of the primary curriculum, so there has been very little emphasis on statistical topics in primary text books, although this has now changed with the inclusion of Handling Data in the National Curriculum. In the more modern schemes, there may well be a fair amount of data handling work, but it can be difficult to find because it will be under a variety of headings, such as pictorial representation, fractions and so on. The coverage varies widely between the various primary schemes and is generally more comprehensive in the recent schemes. The quality of the coverage is more difficult to assess but, usually, the more recently the scheme was published, the more practical the approach.

On the right we include an example of a checklist that teachers may find useful in analysing and assessing their own, or other, maths schemes.

A survey of schemes available appeared in *Teaching Statistics* Vol 14 No 3 (Autumn 1992) and is reproduced here in abridged form with permission of *The Teaching Statistics Trust*.

Data handling in primary mathematical schemes

By Mary Rouncefield, Margaret Rangecroft, Helen Wright and Mariette Roberts

For many pupils their main (or sole?) diet of mathematics is based on a published scheme of work so we decided to review the primary mathematics schemes to see how Data Handling is covered in those books. Between us we managed to cover the following primary schemes:

National Curriculum Ginn Mathematics (Ginn)
Nuffield Mathematics 5–11 (Longman)
Mathematics for Schools (Oliver & Boyd)
Scottish Primary Mathematics Group – S.P.M.G. (Heinemann)
Peak Mathematics (Nelson)
H.B.J. Mathematics Scheme (Harcourt Brace Jovanovich)
Cambridge Primary Mathematics (C.U.P.)

Of these, few came very close to our ideal of statistics as a practical classroom activity; arising from a problem or question posed by the pupils themselves. The process of a

		Text	Check
Collecting		Collecting data	
Representing and analysing		Pictograms	
		Arrow graphs	
		Block graphs	
		Bar charts	
		Stick graphs	
		Straight line graphs	
		Curved line graphs	
		Interrupted line graphs	
		Scales	
		Compound graphs	
		Frequency graphs	
		Pie charts	
		Line of best fit	
		Use of grouped data	
Analysing		Averages (mean, median, mode)	
Interpreting		Interpretation	
		Interpolation and prediction	
Probability		Probability language	
		Equally likely outcomes	
		Probability scale	
		Tree diagrams	

Teachers' checklist for data handling.

statistical investigation has been summarised by Alan Graham as the four stages of PCAI. By working in this way, the data handling done by pupils is related to their own direct experience and their everyday lives. The data they collect are *their* data and they have a genuine interest in following through to the analysis and interpretation stages. Ideally, the process takes place as part of a larger class project encompassing work in other curriculum areas.

In a recent HMI report on National Curriculum Key Stages 1 and 3, data handling was identified as a major gap in the curriculum content actually being received by pupils. HMIs were also worried that many pupils were not gaining sufficient experience in using and applying mathematics (Attainment Target 1). It was with these ideas in mind, that we undertook our survey of the primary mathematics schemes. Of those we reviewed, H.B.J. came the nearest to a genuinely investigative approach.

The scheme is based on mathematical activities within six themes for children to work on in each year. These themes include: Shops, Where We Live, The Park, Fairs, Ourselves, Our School and so on.

Data handling arises naturally within each theme and the themes can be expanded into topic work covering other curriculum areas. H.B.J. does cover the data handling required by the National Curriculum with a couple of minor exceptions. There is though, little awareness shown of the difference between qualitative and quantitative data. In particular, discrete numerical data is not specifically discussed. This is in fact a major flaw in most other schemes and in the National Curriculum document itself. Unfortunately, some teachers may themselves be unaware that such a distinction exists. Generally though, the H.B.J. materials are highly praised for their coverage of data handling and their investigative approach. Both calculator and computer work is integrated into the theme work, with use made of LOGO and databases. Specific reference is also made to AT1 'Using and Applying Mathematics'.

Other schemes are generally less investigative in style and had larger gaps in the data handling actually covered. Some claim (in their advertising materials) to cover topics or techniques which actually do not appear at all. (Could it be that the authors are unfamiliar with the National Curriculum terminology?) Often there were gaps in the pupils' materials which publishers have (belatedly) tried to plug with suggestions in the teachers' notes. Ginn Mathematics for example, has some excellent ideas in the pupils reinforcement and enrichment sections which do not appear in the main workbooks.

The Nuffield Mathematics 5–11 scheme is very attractive and colourful, but as in most schemes, pupils work through set exercises and activities. The better ideas for investigations and indeed some of the better explanations appear in the teachers' handbooks. The Pupils' Book 4 contains probability exercises and experiments but no other data handling work. In common with most schemes, data handling is very thin on the ground.

Peak Mathematics and S.P.M.G. are in the process of being rewritten. The existing S.P.M.G. scheme is already an attractive scheme with detailed teachers' materials, but it does not correlate well with the National Curriculum levels recommended for various age groups. Generally, the idea is that materials are pupil-based rather than teacher-led with resource packs providing ready-prepared games and materials.

On the whole though, there were gaps in most schemes; and while pupils are sometimes given the opportunity to collect their own data, they rarely pose their own questions. HMIs note that there was '...an undue reliance on commercial mathematics schemes in most schools'. For the primary pupil this usually means that they spend much of their time doing individual work, with few opportunities for group activities and social interaction. How many pupils ever have a mathematical conversation?

References
Mathematics Key Stages 1 and 3 HMI Inspectorate (HMSO, 1991).
Investigating Statistics Alan Graham (Hodder & Stoughton, 1990)

Much of the work found in texts at the primary stage is concerned with graphical representation and it is difficult to differentiate between the mathematical and statistical aspects of this graphwork. There is, unfortunately, little emphasis on the important area of interpretation and drawing conclusions.

There are also a few text books which deal specifically with statistical topics but many are out of print. A pair of texts of potentially great usefulness are: *Practical Data Handling Books A and B* Glyn Davies (Hodder & Stoughton, 1993). Book A contains activities for Key Stages 1 and 2, Book B contains activities for Key Stages 3 and 4.

Another useful pair of books, containing photocopiable resource material, are: *Handling Data 1* and *Handling Data 2* A. Whitcombe *et al* (Simon & Schuster, 1992).

Reference, topic and teachers' books on statistics

There are very few books readily available in this country which directly support the primary school teacher's work in data handling, although many can be found which provide indirect assistance.

Investigating Statistics: A Beginner's Guide and *Teach Yourself Statistics* Alan Graham (Hodder & Stoughton). These are particularly useful and appropriate as they use the **PCAI** model adopted in this book.

Pictorial Representation and *Probability & Statistics* W. R. Chambers and John Murray (Nuffield Primary Mathematics Guides, 1965). There are some good ideas in these old Nuffield guides, but they are now out of print. Copies can often be found in schools or teachers' centres.

Choosing and Using Charts Gene Zelazny (Video Arts).

Graphs M. Swann (Nottingham University School of Education).

Dale Seymour Publications in the USA have published an excellent series of six books on data handling, under the general heading *Used Numbers*. Whilst they are clearly aimed at the US market and cover grades K–6 (age 5–12 years) there is a wealth of material in them which would be useful to primary teachers in the UK. Titles in the series are:

Counting: Ourselves and Our Families (Grades K–1)
Sorting: Groups and Graphs (Grades 2–3)
Measuring: From Paces to Feet (Grades 3–4)
Statistics: The Shape of the Data (Grades 4–6)
Statistics: Prediction and Sampling (Grades 4–6)
Statistics: Middles, Means and In-Betweens (Grades 5–6)

These books were reviewed in *Teaching Statistics* Vol 14 No 2. Also published by Dale Seymour are the four US *Quantitative Literacy* series books: *Exploring Data*; *Exploring Probability*; *The Art and Techniques of Simulation*; *Exploring Surveys* (more advanced). These are mainly of use at Key Stages 3 and 4 but there are some ideas which can be adapted to earlier years. Both pupils' and teachers' versions are available. Although aimed at secondary level, there are useful ideas for primary work in the first three books. The last book is mainly rather too advanced.

The Open University has useful publications for teachers. Two of the five *Supporting Primary Mathematics* series are: *Handling Data* and *Probability*.

The Schools Pack on Market Research from The Market Research Society contains a Teachers' Guide, case studies and clipboard.

Project on Statistical Education booklets, available from the Centre for Statistical Education, is a series of 24 booklets designed for use in secondary schools. The following selection is particularly suitable for use in primary schools: *Experiments in Probability*; *Games Fair or Foul*; *Larger or Smaller*; *Stem and Leaf*.

Two recent publications on probability in primary schools worth consulting are:
What's the Chance? (BEAM, 1993). This is an activity pack of 18 activity cards, two games cards, an article on teaching probability and a 20 page teachers' manual. It covers Levels 1–6.
P'raps, P'raps Not (ATM, 1993). This book might best be described as a collage of ideas for primary level probability.

Other useful items are:
What Is a Survey? from the American Statistical Association (this is a free booklet). *Counting Visits and Food Items Brought to Young Birds by their Parents* and *Counting Changes in the Population of Birds* from the Royal Society for the Protection of Birds. These are sets of Teachers' Notes.

Spreadsheets and database books

There are several useful books on spreadsheets for the primary teacher and more are appearing in print all the time. *Exploring Mathematics with Spreadsheets* Lulu Healy and Rosamund Sutherland (Blackwell, 1991). This includes case studies and photocopiable activity sheets. Although it is geared more towards secondary level, many ideas within it can be used or adapted for primary schools, especially the upper age range.
Simply Spreadsheets Roger Keeling and Senga Whiteman (KW Publications).
Spreadsheets available from Hertfordshire County Council.
Thinking About Spreadsheets Hilary Povey (NCET).
Handling Data with a Database and Spreadsheet Mike Hammond (Hodder & Stoughton).
Fifty Things to do with Spreadsheets and Databases Mike Hammond (Centre for Statistical Education).
Spreadsheets for Mathematics and Information Andrew Rothery (John Murray). This publication is much more expensive than the others.

Journals and other publications for teachers

Teaching Statistics is an international journal which looks at the teaching of statistics in all its guises; the emphasis is mainly secondary level but there are some articles and sections useful at the primary level. (See addresses section for more details.)

Other journals
Articles on the teaching of statistics are found periodically in journals concerned with mathematics teaching, such as: *Mathematics in School, Mathematics Teaching, Micromath, Strategies* (see addresses section for more details).
Random News from the Centre for Statistical Education is a free newsletter giving details of courses, publications and developments in statistical education. If you would like to be put on the mailing list, write to the Centre.
The Times Educational Supplement has a special issue on mathematics teaching twice a year with articles and reviews. Other subjects are also regularly covered.
Junior Education and *Child Education* are monthly magazines for primary teachers from Scholastic Publications covering all aspects of the primary school curriculum, including data handling.

Data sources

A valuable asset for the teacher engaged in work on data handling is a source of up-to-date *real* data on a variety of subjects which are likely to interest pupils.

Many organisations produce cross-curricular packs. Examples are:
Aspects of World Trade from *The Financial Times.*
Third World Guide from Oxfam.

HMSO has many interesting publications which can be used as sources for data. Examples are: *Safety at School; Highway Statistics; Safety in the Home* and *Cars for Cities.* A list of HMSO publications can be obtained from their office in London or from branches in major cities.
Key Data is a recent innovation from the Central Statistical Office (CSO). It is a booklet providing some basic key statistics across a wide range of topics presented in an attractive format.

Local authority publications
Many local authorities publish statistics about the local area (often called Yearbooks). Also, Census data by regions are available – perhaps from the local library – although the teacher

would need to prepare carefully for work with young children. The data are available on computer disk also. Census material from the Archive Office – available once the data are 100 years old – is a fascinating source for local history studies. Admittedly, it is a chore for the teacher to interpret and extract the data and enter the information into a computer, but thereafter it provides an invaluable resource, especially once data for two or three different years are transcribed.

Publications from national bodies

Many national bodies such as the Forestry Commission and National Parks publish their figures. Road accident and crime data can often be obtained from the local police. The Fire Service and Electricity Boards and similar services may have statistical information or even software suitable for schools.

The World Bank publishes a set of World Tables which deal mainly with the economics of various countries. It is sometimes possible to access the results of research into, for example, smoking. The Family Policy Studies Centre produce information sheets 'Children under Five' and 'Children' which contain a lot of data. The Consumers' Association's *Which?* series can be useful both for ideas and for data. The two books *Newspapers and Mathematics* and *Newspapers in Education* are available from The Newspaper Society.

Interesting data are available from the many pressure groups and charitable foundations, such as the World Wide Fund for Nature, CAFOD and Save the Children. The Meteorological Office can provide a variety of teaching and reference materials, including curriculum-linked resource packs, wallcharts and leaflets. Contact their Education Service for details.

Fact books

Facts in Focus (Penguin).
World Almanac and Book of Facts (Pan, 1993).
World Almanac (Newspaper Enterprise Association, USA).
Sporting Year Books (soccer, rugby, cricket – found in many bookshops).
Guinness Book of Records.
Guinness Book of Answers.

Miscellaneous publications

Mathematics in Sport (Eigen Publications, based at Sheffield Hallam University) is a series of booklets, some of which include raw data, as well as ideas for teachers on how to analyse it both statistically and mathematically. *World Data* – disks of data prepared by Brian Hudson are available through the York University Centre for World Education. *Teaching Statistics.* This journal has a 'Data Bank' section in each issue, which provides a set of data and suggestions on approaches to analysing the information. Some of these are suitable for primary school work.

Local and national newspapers should not be overlooked; as well as the tables in the sporting pages, sections, such as cars and houses for sale, which contain a wealth of data.

Warning

A final word of warning: it is important to set out with a clear question to answer in mind, and not have the children simply extract and display data without real purpose. Points to consider when providing a set of real data are that it should be of interest to the pupils and should be up to date, unless they are the focus of historical activity.

Workcards and worksheets

The Office of Population Censuses and Surveys (OPCS) *People in Britain* series: *Social Studies in the Census*; *Computer Studies in the Census*; *Geography in the Census* and *History in the Census*

This series, based on the 1991 Census data, comprises the four topic packs above. Each contains factsheets, workcards and facsimile documents, together with Teachers' Notes. Bedfordshire Foundation Mathematics Group (BFMG) produce *Watching TV*, a worksheet from BFMG's *Sport and Leisure* series.

Apparatus

Fortunately, much of the apparatus for teaching statistics consists of everyday objects which are relatively cheap to buy. Apparatus such as coins, playing cards, dice and drawing pins should be no problem to obtain. Equipment such as micrometers, weighing scales and stopwatches may already be available in some schools, or perhaps can be borrowed from parents or local firms. Household items such as cartons can also be useful.

Many educational suppliers sell some apparatus specially for statistics, but it does tend to be expensive and rather limited in its range. Most supply dice, spinners, sampling bottles and counters. These are all useful and fairly versatile.

Most simple apparatus can be produced by teachers themselves without too much difficulty. The teacher can also arrange to have the class make their own simple apparatus which can be a valuable experience in its own right. On the other hand, it may be possible to find a firm or parents willing to design and build equipment to your own specifications.

Random number generators can be made from a ten-faced die, from a spinner or even from a can with the numbers 0 – 9 around the rim which can be rolled along the ground. Asymmetrical dice can be made from modelling material. A little ingenuity goes a long way!

NES Arnold produce a range of relevant products including:

Dice: Loaded, blank, giant foam, giant rubber, numbered, number/+/- .

Spinners: For arithmetic, for probability (with different overlays and allowing the user to mark as desired).

Binostat: A 'maze' down which small balls are dropped and undergo diversions before ending up in different positions.

Probability Kit: A variety of interesting equipment including a binostat.

NES Arnold Probability Kit: A set of six board games, with pupil and teacher workcards.

DIME Project Probability Pack A: Six sets of workcards, and six sets of four sealed shakers containing dice and counters, recording sheets and a Teachers' Guide.

DIME Project Probability Pack B: Six sets of workcards, and six sets of four sealed shakers containing coloured beads, recording sheets and a Teachers' Guide.

Reaction Ruler: This is a very simple but ingenious piece of apparatus which can be used for practical work. It is essentially a ruler which is held vertically by one person, released and has to be caught by another. The time taken to react can be read off directly from the ruler by noting whereabouts on the ruler the person catches it. Teacher's Notes are supplied.

Multilink cubes, Histogram board and Pegboard: Small cubes which link together and can be displayed on a desk in a special holder as three-dimensional bar graphs or fixed to a pegboard to illustrate a scattergraph.

See NES Arnold's equipment catalogue for further details.

The Mathematical Association (MA) sells several different kinds of dice, with various numbers of faces, and even loaded dice which favour six (or one).

Invicta Education produce a lot of educational material for measuring, sorting and probability. Examples are *Weather Instruments* (barometer, rain gauge, thermometer, hygrometer), *Height Measurer*, *Callipers*, *Scales and Balances*, *Binostat* and a *Probabiltiy Kit*.

Television and radio programmes

There is a good deal of useful material available on both television and radio, both as part of mathematics and in other subject areas. It is worth studying the brochures carefully to ascertain what is in each individual programme and picking out what is most appropriate. The news can be a starting-point for investigations, given some planning.

Games

Games are such an obvious vehicle for teaching statistics and especially probability, that it is surprising that there are not more produced commercially. Although many games have a probability basis there seem to be none currently available specifically designed to aid the teaching of probability.

With many games, such as *Mastermind* or *Hare & Tortoise* or *Fox & Geese*, it is easy to draw out the probability aspects through discussion. It is also possible to devise experimental investigations or utilise games apparatus such a Yahtzee and Roulette. Often adaptation is desirable to simplify the rules and method of scoring so that the underlying probabilities become more obvious and simple to calculate. There are some very useful games to be found in topic materials, such as the *Poverty Game* from Oxfam.
Going for a Century (CIMT, Exeter University) is a useful game in CIMT's *Interactive Mathematics* series.
Mathematical Games (Macmillan Education) is a boxed set of games, some involving probability.
Probability Games in the Classroom (Centre for Statistical Education). There are three A4 booklets in this series.
Games and Activities for Probability at Key Stage 1 and Key Stage 2 (The Isaac Newton Development Centre) – this is a booklet.
Teaching Statistics – descriptions of probabilistic and statistical games are occasionally published in this journal.
Probability (Herefordshire County Council) – this booklet includes games.
Chance & Fortune (part of the PRISM pack from the Mathematical Association).
Mathematical Activities from Poland Jerzy Cwirko-Godycki (ATM). This booklet includes some probability games.

Display material

It is perhaps not surprising that there is very little display material available on statistical topics. Statistics is (or at least should be) such a practical subject that a static representation of it is of limited value.
People in Britain (OPCS) is a set of wallcharts produced to support the material already mentioned in the section of workcards and worksheets, but these are rather complex.
Introducing Graphs (Pictorial Charts Educational Trust) is a set of four wallcharts of which two, the bar graph and the pie chart, are genuinely statistical, but hardly exciting!

Starting Statistics and *Introducing Graphs* (Pictorial Charts Educational Trust) – the first of these is a single poster which illustrates the mean, median and mode.

Far more attractive and useful are displays of the pupils' own work. A graph drawn by the children based on real data collected by themselves will be of far greater interest than a contrived graph constructed simply to illustrate a particular educational point. For example, data concerning mythical children will hold much less interest than data concerning the class members themselves or people they know. At the same time, it is important to avoid the situation where graphs are used simply as a rather colourful way of covering a wall. They should always be accompanied by some written material concerning their interpretation, posing questions about them or presenting comments on them.

Interesting and thought-provoking displays can be produced using advertising material and newspaper graphics. It is important to mount the usually drab material carefully, in order to make it eye-catching enough to attract attention. Pertinent questions – displayed with the cuttings – can focus attention and engender interest (for example, 'Is our town shrinking?' with data on local population trends).

It is now possible to create some excellent computer graphics which can be printed out for use as display material. Modern spreadsheets and databases often have powerful graph-drawing facilities of their own. Colour printers are beginning to become more affordable and can be very useful in producing attractive and informative graphics, particularly for display purposes.

Graph recording sheets

The recording sheets which accompany the DIME Probability Kits are a useful alternative to tallying as a means of recording the results of probability experiments. The recording sheets may be purchased independently of the kit and are suitable for older primary pupils.

Computer software

This is an area where resources are proliferating. One way of keeping up to date is via NCET, which produces a booklet listing available software. Another good source of up-to-date information is the Computer Materials Catalogue from RESOURCE.

The following packages are amongst those currently available.

Databases and spreadsheets

Data Sweet – a spreadsheet/database/ graphics integrated program for young children by Kudlian Software, distributed by Hampshire Microtechnology Centre. (Archimedes)

DIYBase – a flexible database designed for primary children to program and use, from RESOURCE. (BBC B, Master, Compact, Archimedes)

Domesday Database – makes local data available (on land usage, housing, shops and so on) which was collated in the BBC Domesday Schools Project. Contact RESOURCE for details of availability of data for your local area. (BBC B, Master, Compact)

Eureka! and *Advantage* – sophisticated spreadsheet packages from Longman Logotron. (Archimedes)

Excel – a sophisticated spreadsheet/database/ graphics package, from Microsoft but better obtained through the local education authority. (Nimbus, IBM PC, Macintosh)

Find – a database suitable for upper primary/ secondary with good graphing facilities, from RESOURCE. (BBC B, Master, Compact, Nimbus)

First Facts – an easy to use database for the very young. It comes with a sample data file suitable for a project on 'Ourselves' from RESOURCE. (BBC B, Master, Compact)

Grass – a simple database for primary use from Newman College, Birmingham. Compatible with *Grasshopper* spreadsheet. (BBC B, Master, Compact, Nimbus, Archimedes)

Grasshopper – a simple spreadsheet for primary use, from Newman College. Compatible with *Grass* database. (BBC B, Master, Compact, Nimbus)

Junior Find – database suitable for primary schools with good graphing facilities, from RESOURCE. (BBC B, Master)

Key and *Key Plus* – databases with graphic facilities, from 3T Productions. More sophisticated than *Grass*. (BBC B, Master, Nimbus)

Oriel – newer, more powerful database developed from *Quest*, from the Advisory Unit at Hatfield. (Nimbus, IBM PC – using Windows)

Our Facts – a rather old but nevertheless useful very elementary database which can still be found, a Welsh version is also available. (BBC B, Nimbus)

Pigeonhole – a starter spreadsheet for young children. (BBC B)

Pipedream – a spreadsheet/database/graphics integrated program for older children and adults. (Archimedes)

PSS – a primary spreadsheet, from Cambridge Software House Ltd. (BBC Master, Nimbus, IBM PC)

Pinpoint and *Junior Pinpoint* – new database programs from Longman Logotron. *Junior Pinpoint* is particularly suitable for primary schools. It has the facility to design a questionnaire on screen which can then be printed out. The program automatically creates a database suitable for receiving the data from the completed questionnaires. (Archimedes)

Quest – an old database now superseded by *Oriel* but which may still be found, from the Advisory Unit at Hatfield. (BBC B, Master, Compact, Archimedes)

TAG/Invicta produce software which allows children to use IT to learn about themselves, create a database of personal details and write about what they find. *Bodymapper* runs on Macintosh computers and the Acorn A3000. [Details from edIT of London.] Also now available or promised are *Weathermapper, Greenmapper, Dinomapper, Streetmapper, Spacemapper* and *Naturemapp*. MJP Geopacks (a specialist geography supplier) stocks a wide variety of apparatus. One item of interest is their *Automatic Weather Station* which links with a BBC B, Master or Nimbus computer. A free demonstration pack is available, as is their comprehensive catalogue.

Sorting tree software

Branch – from NCET.
Idelta – from ILECC.

Graphing packages

DSHOW – on the *Numbers Games* disk by Anita Straker – from ILECC.

Specific programs

SMILE discs – offer some games and simulations for probability (available from SMILE at the Isaac Newton Development Centre).
SLIMWAM (Some Lessons in Mathematics with a Micro) Discs 1 & 2 (ATM). Include statistical activities.
Times – Program in Teaching with a Micro (Maths 3) from Nottingham University Shell Centre.

CD Rom

Climate of the World (Weather Data Associates).
The World Factbook (Quanta Press).
Acorn produce an Education Directory, which is now available free on CD Rom.

Videodisc

Ecodisc – BBC.
Domesday Project – BBC.

Useful addresses

Advisory Unit for Microtechnology in Education, Endymion Road, Hatfield AL10 8AU.
American Statistical Association, 1429 Duke Street, Alexandria, Virginia 22314-3402, USA.
Association for Teachers of Mathematics (ATM), 7 Shaftesbury Street, Derby DE3 8YB.
BBC Education, White City, London W12 7TS.
BEAM, Block C, Barnsbury Complex, Offord Road, London N1 1QH.
Blackwell Publishers, 108 Cowley Road, Oxford OX4 1JF.
BNFL Education Unit, PO Box 10, Wetherby, West Yorkshire LS23 7EL.

CAFOD, 2 Romero Close, Stockwell Road, London SW9 9TY.
Cambridgeshire Software House Ltd, 6 The Quay, St Ives, Huntingdon PE17 4AR.
Centre for Statistical Education, University of Sheffield, Sheffield S3 7RH.
Chambers (W & R Chambers Ltd), 45 Annandale Street, Edinburgh EH7 4AZ.
CIMT, School of Education, University of Exeter, St Luke's, Exeter EX1 2LU.
Consumers' Association, 2 Marylebone Road, London NW1 4DX.
CSO (Central Statistical Office), Great George Street, London SW1P 3AG.
Dale Seymour Publications, PO Box 10888, Palo Alto, CA 94303-0879, USA.
DIME project – available from NES Arnold.
edIT, 48 Junction Road, London N19 5RD.
Eigen Publications, Sheffield Hallam University, Pond Street, Sheffield S1 1WB.
Family Policy Studies Centre, 231 Baker Street, London NW1 6XE.
The Financial Times Ltd, Number One Southwark Bridge, London SE1 9HL.
Forestry Commission, 231 Corstophine Road, Edinburgh EH12 7AT.
Guinness Publishing, 33 London Road, Enfield, Middlesex EN2 6DJ.
3T Productions, Chapel Studio, 47–49 Waterloo Road, Stockport SK1 3BJ.
Microtechnology Centre, Connaught Lane, Portsmouth PO6 4SJ.
Hertfordshire Mathematics Centre, Hertfordshire County Council, Wheathampstead Education Centre, Butterfield Road, Wheathampstead, St Albans AL4 8PY.
H.B.J. (Harcourt Brace Jovanovich Ltd) 24–28 Oval Road, London NW1 7DX.
HMSO Publications Centre, PO Box 276, London SW8 5DT.
HMSO Books, St Crispins, Duke Street, Norwich NR3 1PD.
Hodder & Stoughton, Mill Road, Dunton Green, Sevenoaks, Kent TN13 2YA.
ILECC, John Ruskin Street, London SE5 0PQ.
Invicta Education, Oadby, Leicestershire LE2 4LB.
Isaac Newton Development Centre, 108A Lancaster Road, London W11 1QS.
Jonathan Press, Unit 8, Teybrook Craft Centre,

Great Tey CO6 1JE.

Longman Group Ltd, Longman House, Burnt Mill, Harlow CM20 2JE.

Longman Logotron Ltd, Unit 124 Cambridge Science Park, Milton Road, Cambridge CB4 4ZS.

Mathematical Association, 259 London Road, Leicester LE2 3BE.

Macmillan Education Ltd, Brunel Road, Houndmills, Basingstoke, Hants RG21 2XS.

Market Research Society, 15 Northburgh Street, London EC1V 0AH.

Meteorological Office Education Services, Johnson House, London Road, Bracknell, Berks RG12 2SZ.

MJP Geopacks, Freepost 23, St Just, Cornwall TR19 7JS.

Murray (John Murray Ltd), 50 Albemarle Street, London W1X 4BD.

National Parks – there are ten National Parks, each of which has an information office:

Brecon Beacons – 7 Glamorgan St, Brecon, Powys LD3 7DP.

Dartmoor – Parke, Haytor Rd, Bovey Tracey, Devon TQ13 9JQ.

Exmoor – Exmoor House, Dulverton, Somerset TA22 9HL.

Lake District – Busher Walk, Kendal, Cumbria LA9 4RH.

Northumberland – Eastburn, South Park, Hexham, Northumberland NE46 1BS.

North Yorkshire Moors – The Old Vicarage, Bondgate, Helmsley, York YO6 5BP.

Peak District – Aldern House, Balsow Road, Bakewell, Derbyshire DE4 1AE.

Pembrokeshire Coast – County Offices, Haverfordwest, Dyfed SA61 1QZ.

Snowdonia – Penrhyndeudraeth, Gwynedd LL48 6LS.

Yorkshire Dales – Yorebridge House, Bainbridge, Leyburn, N Yorks DL8 3BP.

National Council for Educational Technology (NCET), Milburn Hill Road, Science Park, Coventry CV4 7JJ.

NES Arnold Ltd, Ludlow Hill Road, West Bridgford, Nottingham NG2 1BR.

Newman College, Genners Lane, Bartley Green, Birmingham B32 3NT.

Newspaper Society, Bloomsbury House, 74–77 Great Russell St, London WC1B 3DA.

Nottingham University School of Education, University of Nottingham, Nottingham NG7 2RD.

Nottingham University Shell Centre for Mathematical Education, University of Nottingham, Nottingham NG7 2RD.

OPCS (Office of Population Censuses and Surveys), Information Branch, St Catherine's House, 10 Kingsway, London WC2B 6JP.

Open University, Learning Materials Sales Office, PO Box 188, Milton Keynes MK7 6DH.

OXFAM, 274 Banbury Road, Oxford OX2 7DZ.

PAN Macmillan Distribution Ltd, Brunel Road, Houndmills, Basingstoke, Hants RG21 2XS.

Penguin Books Ltd, 27 Wright's Lane, London W8 5TZ.

Pictorial Charts Educational Trust (PCET), 27 Kirchen Road, London W13 0UD.

RESOURCE, Exeter Road, Off Coventry Grove, Doncaster DN2 4PY.

Simon & Schuster Ltd, Campus 400, Maylands Avenue, Hemel Hempstead HP2 7EZ.

RoSPA, Cannon House, The Priory, Queensway, Birmingham B4 6BS.

RSPB, The Lodge, Sandy, Bedfordshire SG19 2DL.

Scholastic Publications Ltd, Villiers House, Clarendon Avenue, Leamington Spa CV32 5PR.

Teaching Statistics details from The Centre for Statistical Education at Sheffield.

Ward Lock Educational, 1 Christopher Road, East Grinstead, West Sussex RH19 3BT.

Which? and similar magazines are available from the Consumers' Association.

West Midlands Police HQ, PO Box 52, Lloyd House, Colmore Circus, Queensway, Birmingham B4 6NQ.

World Bank European Office, 66 Avenue d'Elena, F-75116 Paris, France.

University of York Centre for World Education, Heslington, York YO1 5DD.

Glossary

Average: an average is a useful way of summarising a set of figures into a single figure. It is a 'representative' value and can be calculated in a number of ways. The three most common averages are:
the mode – the value that occurs most often;
the median – if all the values are arranged in order of size from smallest to biggest, the median is the value of the middle one;
the mean – calculated by adding all the values together and dividing by however many values there are.

Categorical data: data, or numerical information, comes in a number of different forms. Categorical data (or category data) shows the number of items that fall into different categories; for example, the number of children with different pets, the number of people with different blood groups, the number of each flavour of crisp sold in the tuck shop, and so on.

Continuous data: certain measures, such as length, weight, time, temperature, and so on, produce 'continuous' data. What makes a measure, such as the weight of a bag of sugar, continuous, is that there are an infinite number of possible weights between which it could be, say, 995g and 1005g. The number of possible weights are limited only by how accurately you choose to perform the measure. (cf., discrete data)

Database: a database is any storage of data, be it a shoebox stuffed with bills, an exercise book containing accounts or a diary full of names and addresses. However, the most powerful databases are where information is stored on a computer. The term 'computer database' has two meanings. The first is a type of software package that is specially set up for the user to store and retrieve information easily (for example, we say that *Junior Pinpoint* is a database package). The second meaning refers to the information that is stored there (for example, a class might make a database of the school sports results).

Discrete data: some measures, such as shoe sizes, prices, numbers of pupils with brown eyes, and so on, produce 'discrete' data. This means that the numbers used to measure with are restricted to a limited set of discrete values. For example, if a bag of sugar cost between 65 and 70 pence, there are only six possibilities – 65p, 66p, 67p, 68p, 69p and 70p. Unlike with continuous measures, 'in-between' measures (for example, a price between 67p and 68p such as 67.129p) simply do not exist, no matter how accurately the price is measured. (cf., continuous data)

Correlation (paired data): paired data occur when two separate measures are taken from each individual item in the sample. For example, a class carrying out a weather survey might measure the temperature and the rainfall each day over a month. Correlation is a measure of how strongly the two variables (in this case, temperature and rainfall) are connected. If correlation is strong, then one of the variables is a good predictor of the other. 'Positive' correlation is where high values in one variable are associated with high values in the other. 'Negative' correlation is where high values in one variable are associated with low values in the other.

Events and outcomes: these are two terms used in probability and they are often confused with each other. An event, sometimes called a 'trial', is where something happens but you don't know in advance what the result will be (for example, tossing a die or coin, closing your eyes and sticking a pin in a football pools coupon, and so on). The outcomes are the possible ways that the event could turn out (for example, tossing a die has six equally-likely outcomes, '1', '2',... '6', tossing a coin has two equally-likely outcomes, 'heads' and 'tails', and so on). Once an event has occurred, there will have been only one outcome, but it could not have been predicted in advance.

Primary and secondary data: primary data refers to information that you measure directly yourself (for example, taking an examination mark from each pupil in the class, measuring the density of different materials in a science experiment, and so on). Secondary data refers to information that has already been collected by someone else but is used as part of your investigation (for example, statistical information taken from a newspaper, magazine or library book).

PCAI cycle: sometimes statistics can be a dreary and mechanical subject where data are collected for the sole purpose of giving pupils practice at drawing graphs and carrying out calculations. If teachers are to preach what is practised by statisticians, and also to motivate their pupils, they will want to encourage them to tackle purposeful investigations. The PCAI cycle describes four common-sense stages that characterise statistical investigations at all levels. They are 'P' – Pose the question, 'C' – Collect the data, 'A' – Analyse the data, 'I' – Interpret the results.

Probability: probability is a measure of uncertainty – in other words, it is a way of assessing the chance of certain outcomes happening. Gamblers tend to measure probability in terms of odds (a three-to-one chance, a one-in-four chance, and so on). Statisticians prefer to rate probabilities on a number scale from zero to one. A probability of zero means the outcome is impossible, a probability of one means the outcome is certain and a probability of 0.5 means the outcome is 'fifty-fifty'.

Spreadsheet: this is a computer software package which allows data to be stored. Graphs and calculations can then easily be performed. The information is entered on to a table consisting of cells arranged in rows and columns. The rows are denoted by numbers and the columns by letters. One of the particular strengths of a spreadsheet is that a formula can be entered into a single cell which can then be replicated (i.e. copied) across many columns or down many rows.

Variable: measures like 'height', 'temperature', 'rainfall', 'shoe size', 'age', and so on, are known as variables. To take rainfall as an example, measurements that are taken every day will produce various different values. It is this variety of different possible values that gives rise to the name 'variable'. Variables can be categorised in different ways. For example, one useful distinction is between discrete and continuous variables (see above).

Index